EXPLORING THE
Earth and Moon

Patrick Moore

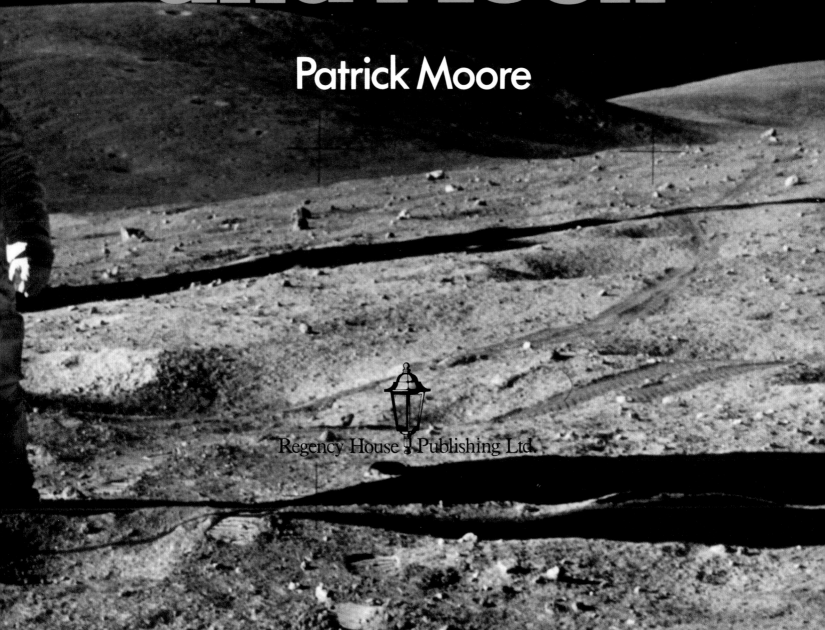

EXPLORING THE
Earth
and Moon

Patrick Moore

Regency House Publishing Ltd.

Published by
Regency House Publishing Limited
The Grange, Grange Yard
London, SE1 3AG

Copyright © 1991, 1996
Regency House Publishing Limited

ISBN 1 85361-447-5

Printed in China

Title Page: Astronaut Charles
N. Duke Jr. saluting the U.S.
flag during the Apollo 16 lunar
mission in 1972.
Right: A shot of the lunar
landscape, showing the heavily
cratered surface.

Contents

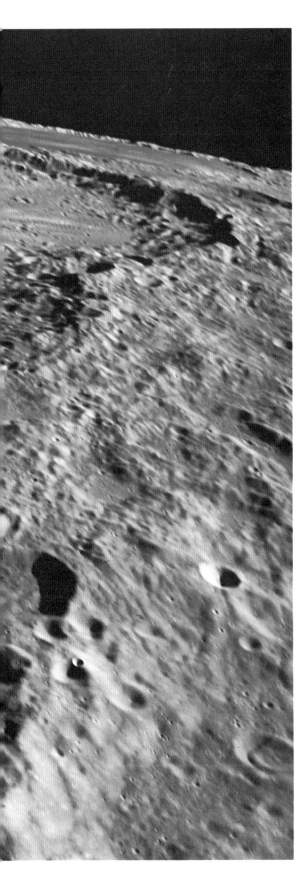

The Earth in Space

A Meteosat image of Earth with the continent of Africa clearly visible.

How old is the Earth? How was it born? How important is it in the universe as a whole, and how long can it survive? Was the Moon once part of the Earth, and why has it no air or water today?

These are only some of the questions which almost everyone must have asked at one time or another. In trying to answer them, we have to bring in various branches of science – not only astronomy and geology, but also chemistry, biology, physics and many others. Even today there are still many problems which remain to be solved, though we have made a surprising amount of progress over the last few years.

The Earth is a globe almost 12,880km (8,000 miles) in diameter, moving round the Sun. The Earth-Sun distance (known officially as the astronomical unit) is approximately 150 million kilometres (93 million miles). This may sound a long way, and in our everyday experience this is certainly true, but it is not far to an astronomer, who has to reckon with tremendous distances and vast spans of time. Nobody can really appreciate these huge quantities, and all we can do is to try to accept them.

The Sun is a star. It is by no means distinguished, and modern astronomers even relegate it to the status of a yellow dwarf; it appears splendid in our skies because on the cosmical scale it is so close. Many of the stars visible on any clear night are a great deal larger, hotter and more luminous than our Sun, but they are also a great deal farther away. Indeed, they are so remote that to measure their distances in miles or kilometres would be hopelessly clumsy, just as it would be awkward to give the distance between London and New York in millimetres. Instead, astronomers use a unit called the light-year, which is the distance travelled by a ray of light in one year. Since light flashes along at approximately 300,000km/sec (186,000 miles/sec), a light-year is equal to 9,460,000,000,000 kilometres (5,880,000,000,000 miles). Even the nearest star beyond the Sun is over four light-years away.

Because of this, the stars look like mere specks of light, and their positions relative to each other change so slowly that to all intents and purposes the star-patterns or constellations remain the same over periods of many human lifetimes. The constellations which we see today – Orion, the Great Bear, the Dragon and the rest – are virtually the same as those which must have been seen by the Pilgrim Fathers, the Roman Emperors or even the builders of the Egyptian Pyramids. Our star-system or Galaxy contains around 100,000 million suns, and beyond we can see other galaxies, so that the observable universe is quite inconceivably vast.

Our own particular part of space, the Solar System, is made up of one star (the Sun), the nine planets, and various bodies of lesser importance, such as the moons or satellites, the minor planets or asteroids, comets and meteoroids. There are nine known planets, divided into two well-marked groups. First there are four relatively small, rocky worlds: Mercury, Venus, the Earth and Mars. Beyond the orbit, or path, of Mars comes a wide gap in which move thousands of dwarf worlds known as asteroids; further out, beyond the asteroid zone, we come to the four giants Jupiter, Saturn, Uranus and Neptune, together with another midget, Pluto, which seems to be something of a maverick and is in a class of its own. There are grave doubts today as to whether it should be classed as a proper planet.

The planets are not self-luminous, but shine only by reflecting the light of the Sun. The first five are conspicuous naked-eye objects, and have been known since very early times; the Greeks, centuries before the time of Christ, knew all about their movements (even though most of them made the serious mistake of believing that they revolved around the Earth, not around the Sun). Venus and Jupiter are brighter than any of the stars, and so is Mars when at its best, and Saturn, too, is very prominent; Mercury has the disadvantage of remaining in the same part of the sky as the Sun, so that with the naked eye it can be seen only when low in the west after sunset or low in the east before dawn. Three more distant planets have been discovered in

The size and scale of cosmic systems showing the place of the Earth not only in our Solar System but also in our galaxy.

A montage of photographs taken by various NASA spacecraft, displaying the smaller planets and larger moons of the Solar System at the same scale. Io, Europa, Ganymede and Callisto are Jupiter's larger moons. Titan is Saturn's larger moon.

modern times: Uranus in 1781, Neptune in 1846 and Pluto as recently as 1930. Uranus can just be seen with the naked eye if you know where to look for it, but to see Neptune and Pluto you have to use an optical aid.

The four giant planets are not solid and rocky. Undoubtedly they have solid cores, but most of their globes are thought to be liquid, while their deep atmospheres are gaseous, with hydrogen the most abundant constituent (which is not in the least surprising, because hydrogen is the most plentiful element in the universe). Each planet has its own special points of interest, and by now all of them apart from Pluto have been surveyed from close range by unmanned space-craft, while controlled landings have been made on Venus and Mars.

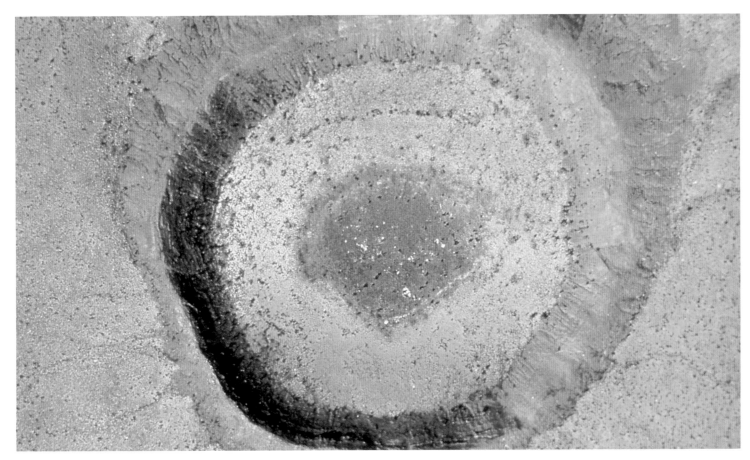

The distances of the planets from the Sun range between 60 million kilometres (36 million miles) (the average distance of Mercury) out to 4,494 million kilometres (2,793 million miles) for Neptune. Generally speaking their orbits are not very different from circles, though Pluto is an exception; Mercury takes only 88 Earth-days to complete one journey around the Sun, while Neptune takes almost 165 Earth-years. Like the Earth, they are spinning on their axes; Venus has the longest rotation period (243 Earth-days) while Jupiter spins round once in less than ten hours.

Most of the planets are attended by satellites. The Earth, of course, has one – our familiar Moon; Saturn has 17 known satellites, Jupiter 16, Uranus 15, Neptune eight and Mars two, while Pluto's attendant, Charon, seems to be about half the size of Pluto itself. Only Mercury and Venus are solitary travellers in space.

The asteroids, most of which keep strictly to the zone between the paths of Mars and Jupiter, are relatively small;

only one (Ceres) is as much as 800 kilometres (500 miles) in diameter, and only one (Vesta) is ever visible with the naked eye. The total membership of the swarm may be well over 40,000, but there are not many asteroids with diameters of more than a few kilometres. There are some tiny bodies which swing away from the main swarm, and may come close to the Earth, so that there is always the danger of a collision – and there is indeed a serious theory that a cosmic impact around 65,000,000 years ago caused such a change in the Earth's climate that the dinosaurs, which had been lords of the world for so long, simply could not cope with the new conditions, and died out (I will have more to say about this later). There are also collisions with meteorites, which are made up of stone or rock, and which almost certainly come from the asteroid belt, so that there is probably no difference between a large meteorite and a small asteroid. Impact craters are known, of which the most famous on Earth is Meteor Crater in Arizona,

An aerial view of Wolf Meteorite Crater in Western Australia.

almost 1·6km (1 mile) wide. There is no doubt that the Arizona crater was produced by a meteorite which hit the desert well over 20,000 years ago.

The most erratic members of the Solar System are comets, which may become spectacular, but are not nearly so important as they look. Most of them move around the Sun in highly eccentric paths, not in the least like the orbits of the planets. Basically a comet is a lump of 'dirty ice' only a few kilometres across, and when at a great distance from the Sun it is inert; but when it draws inward the ice begins to evaporate, and the comet may produce a head or coma together with a tail. To be more precise, there may be more than one tail; some are made up of gas, others of 'dust'. As a comet moves along it leaves a dusty track behind it, and when one of these dust-particles comes into the Earth's upper air it burns away by friction against the atmosphere, producing the streak of luminosity which we call a meteor or shooting-star. Note that there is no connection between meteors, which are cometary débris, and meteorites, which are asteroidal. It is also worth noting that comets lie well beyond the atmosphere, so that they do not shift perceptibly against the starry background except over periods of hours. If you see something moving quite obviously in the night sky, it is certainly not a comet.

Some comets have periods of a few years, so that we always know when and where to expect them, but most of these are too faint to be seen without a teles-cope. Really brilliant comets have periods of many centuries, so that they are apt to take us by surprise; the last conspicuous visitor of this kind was West's Comet of 1976 (so named because it was discovered by the Danish astronomer Richard West). The only bright comet which we can predict is Halley's, which was last close to the Sun in 1986 and will be back in 2061 – though we must admit that as a spectacle it was very disappointing 'last time round'.

Comets are of very slight mass compared with planets or even major satellites. Whether or not they have played a significant rôle in the story of the Earth is not certain; some astronomers believe so, and it has even been suggested that life was brought to our world by way of a comet.

Now let us turn to our faithful companion, the Moon. Apart from the Sun it is the most splendid object in the sky, and it dominates the night for parts of every month, so that we sometimes find it hard to believe that the Moon is a very junior member of the Solar System. It is a mere 3,476km (2,160 miles) in diameter, so that if you represent the Earth by a tennis-ball the Moon will be no larger than a table-tennis ball. Like the planets, it has no light of its own, and on average its surface reflects only about 7 per cent of the sunlight falling upon it, so that as a cosmic mirror the Moon is very inefficient. Its mean distance from the Earth is a little over 400,000km (238,000 miles), which is less than ten times the distance round the Earth's equator, and

The starkly beautiful surface of the Moon eerily illuminated in this photograph of astronaut Harrison Schmitt (Apollo 17) standing by a boulder in the Taurus-Littrow valley.

it takes 27.3 days to complete one orbit.

Though they are so closely linked, the Earth and the Moon are very different, mainly because the Moon is so much the smaller of the two. Put the Earth in one pan of a gigantic pair of scales, and you will need 81 Moons to balance it. This means that the Moon's pull of gravity is much less than that of the Earth, and it has been unable to hold on to any atmosphere it may once have had (a point to which I will return later). The modern Moon is airless, lifeless and waterless, with bone-dry lava-plains which we still mis-call 'seas', together with mountains, valleys, ridges and thousands upon thousands of walled circular structures which we know as craters. Yet puny though the Moon may be, it is still a very substantial body. In the Solar System there are four satellites – three in Jupiter's family, one in Saturn's – which are larger than the

Moon, but all these move round giant worlds, so that all in all it may be better to class the Earth-Moon system as a double planet rather than as a planet and a satellite.

In one respect the Earth is unique in the Solar System: it is the only planet which is suited to life of our kind. Of the rest, Venus is too hot and has the wrong sort of atmosphere; Mars, too, has an unsuitable atmosphere and is unpleasantly cold; Mercury and most of the satellites of the other planets have no atmospheres at all, while the giants do not even have solid surfaces. Moreover, there is no reason to believe that conditions on the Earth will change much for a very long time in the future, so that we have been given a good home – even though we are not being particularly careful about looking after it!

Dreams of reaching the Moon go back

for many centuries, but only in our own time has it become a reality. The first unmanned rockets were sent there in 1959, and ten years later Neil Armstrong, from Apollo 11, made his never-to-be-forgotten 'one small step' on to the lava-plain still called by its old, picturesque name of the Sea of Tranquillity. Other missions followed between 1969 and 1972, and there seems every chance that by the year 2000 we will have a fully-fledged Lunar Base. Yet the Moon has lost none of its romance.

In learning about the Moon, we are also learning more about the Earth. Let us now look back in time to see whether we can decide when and how the two worlds were formed.

The Apollo 11 Lunar Module in its ascent stage, 21 July 1969, photographed from the Command and Service Module. The lunar coordinates below are 102 degrees east, 1 degree north.

Formation of the Earth

Before discussing the formation of the Earth, we must go back even further in time and look at the way in which the universe itself came into existence. To be candid, nobody knows. All we can say is that according to modern theory, the universe came into existence at one particular moment in a 'big bang' sometime between 15,000 million and 20,000 million years ago. Just how this happened is a complete mystery, and neither can we say where the 'big bang' took place. If space, time and matter came into being at the same instant, then it is fair to say that the 'big bang' happened everywhere.

At first the universe was very small and incredibly hot, but as soon as it had been formed it started to expand, and galaxies were produced. Stars were born inside the galaxies, and the universe began to take on what we call a recognizable form. Some of the stars were short-lived, and soon exploded, sending their material away into space. Other stars were then formed from the blown-off material, and one of these stars was our own Sun, aged probably c.5,000 million years

The Sun is gaseous. It is large enough to contain over a million bodies the volume of the Earth, and it is producing its own energy, not because it is 'burning' in the manner of a coal fire but because of changes going on deep inside it. Near the Sun's core the temperature is at least 14,000,000°C, and the pressure is enormous. Much of the globe is made up of hydrogen (which, as we have noted, is much the commonest of all the elements), and near the centre of the Sun the hydrogen is being changed into another element, helium. It takes four

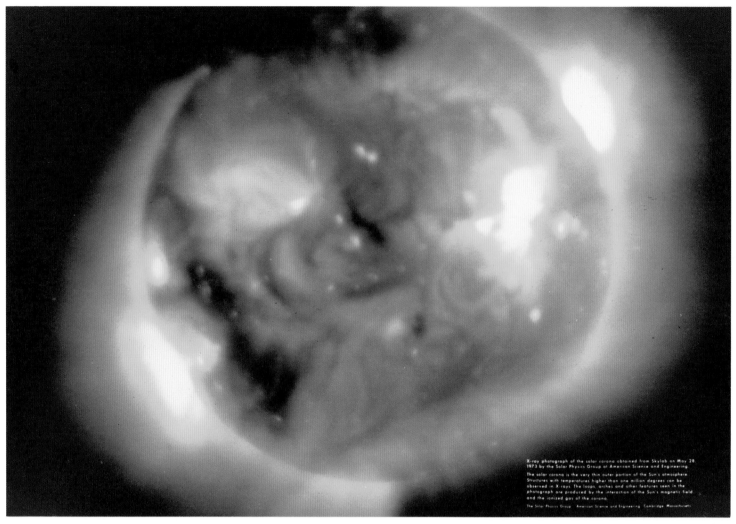

X-ray photograph of the solar corona obtained from Skylab on May 28, 1973 by the Solar Physics Group at American Science and Engineering.

The solar corona is the very thin outer portion of the Sun's atmosphere. Structures with temperatures higher than one million degrees can be observed in X-rays. The loops, arches and other features seen in the photograph are produced by the interaction of the Sun's magnetic field and the ionized gas of the corona.

The Solar Physics Group · American Science and Engineering · Cambridge Massachusetts

This image of the Sun was formed using X-ray wavelengths only. The corona, which is the hot outer layer of the Sun's atmosphere, is clearly visible. The photograph was taken from Skylab.

*The English 'billion' is one million million, while the more common American billion is one thousand million. Since there is danger of confusion, I have avoided using the term 'billion' at all.

'bits' of hydrogen to create one 'bit' of helium, and each time this happens a little energy is released, with loss of mass. It is this energy which keeps the Sun shining, while the loss of mass amounts to over 4,000 million kilograms/sec (4 million tons/sec. The Sun 'weighs' much less now than when you opened this book.

However, the Sun has so much mass that its available store of hydrogen fuel will last for several thousands of millions of years yet before running low, and we can also work out how long the process has been going on. Since the Sun must be older than the Earth, we can agree that the age of the Earth itself is well over 4,000 million years. The best value we can give today is 4,600 million years, though nobody would pretend that this figure is at all precise.*

There are various ways of estimating the age of the Earth. One of these involves the well-known phenomenon of radioactivity. There are some heavy elements which change their nature at a constant rate, without any outside interference, and one of these is uranium, which decays very slowly into lead. We know the rate of change, and we can also distinguish uranium-lead from ordinary lead, so that if we find the two substances together we can tell how long the process has been going on. Uranium found in rocks proves that in some cases the rocks must be over 3,000 million years. This at once gives us a lower limit to the age of the Earth, because in its early history the globe was not solid enough for rocks to form.

There is also a great deal to be learned from the study of fossils, a branch of science known as paleontology. Fossils

An artist's impression of the nebular formation of the Solar System from a cloud of dust and gas by a process of accretion.

are the remains of plants and animals found embedded in rocks; they are of many kinds (to give even a rough classification would take many pages), and they can be dated. Some fossils are well over 500 million years old.

All this seems obvious enough today, but there has always been a strong opposition to the idea of a very ancient Earth. Most of the objections are based upon the Bible, and it is claimed that everything is summed up in the Book of Genesis: God created the world in seven days, and no more need be said. Working along these lines, the seventeenth-century Irish archbishop James Ussher stated that the world had been created at precisely ten o'clock in the morning of 26 October, 4004 B.C. Later, it was even suggested that fossils had been divinely produced simply to trick inquiring scientists. One sad story involves a German professor, Johann Beringer of the University of Würzburg, who was firmly convinced that fossils were reasonably modern, and paid his students to collect them. Human nature being what it is, the students 'planted' fossils made of baked clay, and decorated them with drawings and inscriptions. Beringer published an elaborate book about them in 1727, but his faith was shattered when he found a fossil with his own name written upon it. He spent the rest of his life trying to buy and destroy all the remaining copies of his book!

Charles Darwin's book *The Origin of Species*, published in 1859, sparked off another furious argument. It was bitterly attacked by the Church, because Darwin claimed – correctly – that human beings and animals have the same ancestors (which is not the same as saying that men are descended from monkeys; Darwin never suggested anything of the kind). Despite all the evidence, some people refused to be convinced. In 1925 the State of Tennessee prosecuted a school teacher, Thomas Scopes, for daring to support 'Darwinism', and the Act prohibiting the teaching of the theory of evolution was not repealed in Tennessee until 1967. There has been another case of persecution, in its most savage form, very recently. In 1990 a well-known Sudanese biologist, Professor Farouk Mohamed Ibrahim, was arrested and tortured at Khartoum because his teaching of evolution offended the Islamic religious leaders.

There can be no doubt that the Sun is the true parent of the Earth and the other planets. The first really scientific theory of the origin of the Solar System was

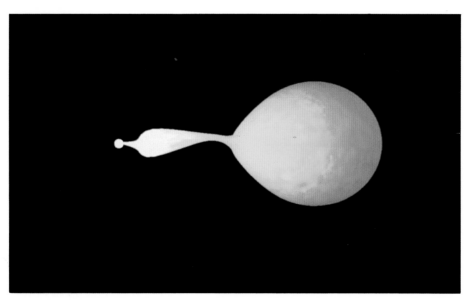

Above: Computer graphic showing how a passing star might have pulled from the Sun a tongue of material which later broke up and became the planets.

Far right: The Trifid Nebula M20. Our own Sun was born in a cloud of gas similar to this. 40,000 light years across, this nebula contains enough gas to form thousands of stars.

published by the French astronomer Laplace in 1796. On this so-called 'Nebular Hypothesis', the Sun condensed slowly out of the material spread through space, and as it shrank it threw off rings, each of which condensed into a planet. It sounded reasonable enough, but mathematicians found serious flaws in it, and for many years Laplace's theory was ignored, though now we have returned to a not dissimilar theory.

Another idea, popular until less than fifty years ago, involved a 'close encounter' between the Sun and a passing star. It was suggested that a wandering star approached the Sun and raised huge tides in it, so that a long tongue of material was pulled away from the Sun's surface; as the wanderer moved away, the tongue was left whirling around the Sun, and broke up into drops, each of which produced a planet. It was pointed out that the tongue would have been cigar-shaped, and that the most massive planets, Jupiter and Saturn, are in the middle part of the Solar System, where the thickest part of the cigar would have been.

Sir James Jeans, well remembered today not only for his popular and technical books but also for his broadcasts, was the champion of the passing-star theory, but again the mathematicians found so many weaknesses in it that it too was abandoned. The same fate overtook Sir Fred Hoyle's proposal that the planets were formed from a com-panion star to the Sun which exploded, sending out the débris which built up into planets.

Modern theories do away with the need for a companion star, exploding or otherwise. What seems to have happened is that as the youthful Sun condensed, it was associated with a vast cloud of dust and gas – a 'solar nebula' – which spread out into a rotating, flattened disk. Regions of greater density began to collect into 'clumps', under the influence of gravity, and as soon as a 'clump' had become massive enough it was able to pull in material from around it, so that the planets built up by a process known as accretion, while the central part of the solar nebula turned into the present Sun. In areas close to the newly-formed Sun the heat was intense, and very light elements such as hydrogen and helium were driven outwards; at greater distances the temperatures were lower, so that planets could collect and hold a much greater amount of hydrogen.

This theory is convincing in many ways. It explains why the giants contain so much hydrogen, and also why the planets move around the Sun in the same direction in much the same plane, so that if you draw a plan of the Solar System on a flat table you are not very far wrong. Material which was 'left over' during the planet-forming period now remains in the form of asteroids, comets and meteoroids, together with a surprisingly large quantity of interplanetary 'dust'.

The change in our outlook has one very important result. The stars are widely spread-out in space; the nearest of them, Proxima Centauri in the southern part of the sky, is over four light-years away (corresponding to around 24 million million miles), and there are not many stars within a dozen light-years of us. If Jeans' theory had been correct, then Solar Systems would have been very rare in the Galaxy, because close encounters between two stars are most unusual; it would even have been possible that the Sun's family of planets would have been the only one. But upon present theories, planetary systems are likely to be very common. The Sun is a very ordinary star, and there is no reason to believe that its system is in any way exceptional.

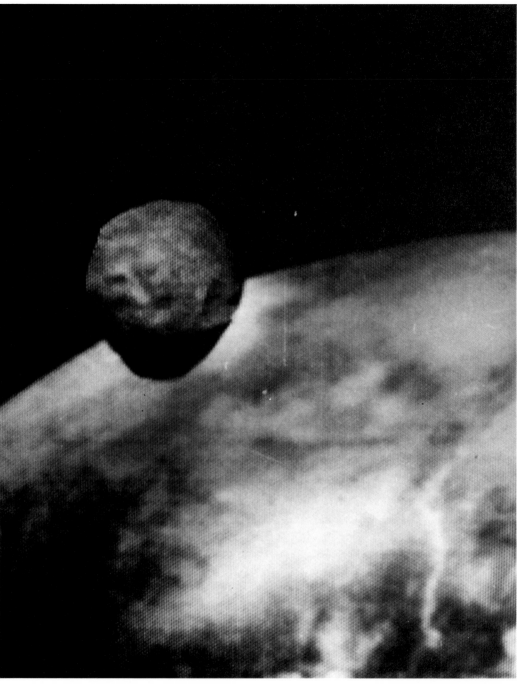

The larger satellites of the planets
were probably formed by the same kind
of process, though some of the smaller
satellites are different; for example the
two dwarf attendants of Mars, Phobos
and Deimos, are only a few miles across,
and may be ex-asteroids which wandered
too close to Mars. But the Moon may be a
special case.

According to Sir George Darwin, son
of Charles Darwin, the Moon and the
Earth used to be a single body, spinning
quickly round on its axis. As it rotated it
first became egg-shaped and then dumb-
bell-shaped; finally the 'neck' of the dumb-
bell broke, and the Moon moved out
to become an independent body, though
it could never break free from the Earth's
pull of gravity. Slowly it moved away,
until it had reached its present distance.

The American astronomer W.H. Pickering even believed that the deep scar now filled by the Pacific Ocean indicates the place where the Moon broke away.

Again this sounds convincing, but there is little doubt that it is wrong. Certainly the Pacific basin cannot be involved, because if we represent the Earth by a tennis-ball we find that the depth of the Pacific will be less than the thickness of a postage stamp. In any case, the mathematicians have stepped in once more, and have found so many weaknesses in the whole theory that it has generally been given up. There are various modifications, some of which involve a violent collision with a wandering body, and there are also suggestions that the Moon was once an independent planet in its own right which was captured after an encounter with the Earth; but all in all, it seems reasonable to think that the Earth and the Moon were formed from the same part of the solar nebula at the same time. The difference between the Earth and the Moon is due entirely to the Moon's lower mass. Moreover, we have been able to analyze the lunar rocks brought home by the Apollo astronauts and the Russian automatic space-craft, and we have confirmed that the Moon, like the Earth, has an age of about 4,600 million years.

It is all very different from Archbishop Ussher's 'creation date' of 4004 B.C., but although there are still many details to be cleared up we can at least be confident that we now have a good idea of the way in which our world was born.

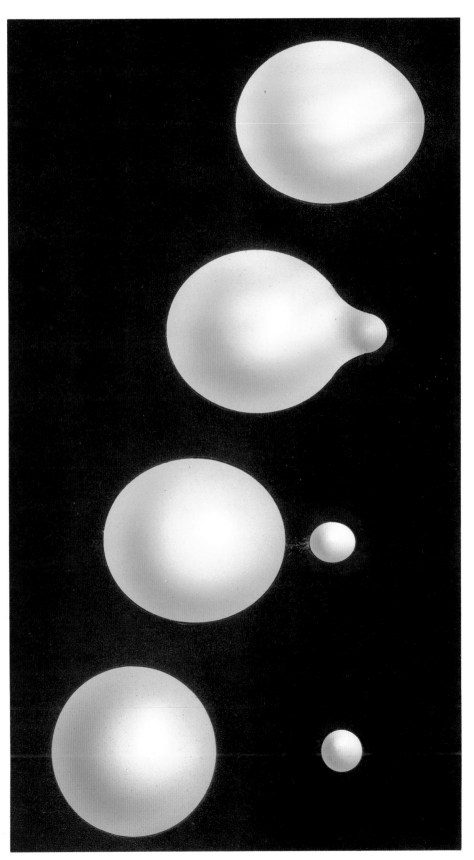

The Story of the Earth

We do not know nearly as much as we would like to do about the very early part of the Earth's history, because until we come to the time when rocks were formed, and can be dated, we have comparatively little to guide us. At least we can be sure that the young Earth was hot, and took a long time to cool down, particularly as radioactive elements give off heat as they decay. We are also sure that the original atmosphere, made up chiefly of hydrogen, was lost. The temperature was too high for hydrogen to be held down, and it simply escaped into space, so that there was a time when the world was airless.

This did not last, because of volcanic activity. A new atmosphere was formed from the gases and vapour sent up from inside the Earth, and this is the 'air' which we breathe today, though its composition has changed since very early times. In particular, the 'new' atmosphere contained little free oxygen, but a great deal of the heavy gas carbon dioxide. (If we could go into a time machine and project ourselves backward by, say, 500 million years, we would be unable to

An eruption of the volcano on Karkar Island, Papua New Guinea. The gases emitted by such eruptions were responsible for the formation of Earth's early atmosphere.

breathe.) Later, when plants spread on to the land, everything was altered; plants take in carbon dioxide and give off oxygen, so that gradually the atmosphere became breathable.

The oceans were also formed at an early stage, and it may be that there was a long spell of continuous rainfall. Only when there was enough surface water, and the temperature had fallen sufficiently, could life begin. And here we come to another problem which has yet to be solved: just when and how did life begin?

Just as we can say nothing definite about the Big Bang, so we are quite unable to explain the origin of life. We know how living things are made up, and we have found that they all depend upon one particular type of atom, carbon; it is fair to say that according to all the available evidence, life anywhere in the universe will be carbon-based, so that it will not be completely alien even though it might look quite unlike anything we find on Earth. (Remember, though, that life can take many forms; there is not much resemblance between a man and an earwig – but both are based upon carbon.) We are also sure that living matter was created from non-living matter. We have been unable to produce life artificially, and we may never be able to do so, but Nature managed it, and most scientists believe that life began in our warm seas well over 500 million years ago. By the start of the geological Cambrian Period there was plenty of primitive marine life, and we can identify its fossils.

Not everyone has agreed with this picture. In the early part of our own century the Swedish chemist Svante Arrhenius, whose work was good enough to win him a Nobel Prize, suggested that life did not begin here, but was brought to Earth by way of a meteorite. This idea never became popular, because it is not easy to see how life could appear and survive in a small lump of stone or iron, but the principle has been revived in recent years by Sir Fred Hoyle and his colleague Chandra Wickramasinghe, who believe that life was carried to the Earth not by a meteorite, but by a comet.

Comets, as we have seen, are icy objects which wander far from the Sun.

Above: The first free oxygen on Earth was probably generated by bacteria. These stromatolites at Shark Bay, Western Australia, are composed of colonies of cyanobacteria, descendants of those early oxygen-generating bacteria. The bacteria also secrete calcium carbonate and become solidified. These colonies can be up to 3000 million years old.

According to the Dutch astronomer Jan Oort, there is a whole 'cloud' of them moving round the Sun at a distance of about one light-year, so that the comets which we see plunging into the inner part of the Solar System have been pulled out of the Dort Cloud by the gravitational action of some passing body. But Hoyle and Wickramasinghe claim that some comets, at least, come from far beyond

Left: A fragment of the meteorite which fell at Barwell, England, in 1966.

'Smoking Cliffs', Halemaumau Crater, Hawaii. It was in just such an environment, as the Earth cooled, that the first life forms evolved.

the Solar System, and are not true members of the Sun's family, and that when they come close to the Earth, they can deposit living matter in the upper air. They go so far as to claim that our oceans were brought here by comets, and that even today some epidemics ranging from measles to smallpox are due to bacteria put into the atmosphere by passing comets.

Not many people agree. It seems that the whole theory raises far more problems than it solves, and the 'comet epidemics' are not taken seriously by medical experts, but it is certainly true to say that the origin of life on Earth is still very much of a mystery.

The Earth is a restless place. The outlines of the lands and seas change slowly but dramatically; mountains are raised, while other ranges are levelled by erosion, and we also have to reckon with volcanic eruptions and major earthquakes. The climates change too. It is only about 10,000 years since the end of the last Ice Age, when the world was a much colder place than it is today. We have been able to build up a reasonably good picture of what has happened during the last 600 million years or so, but the further back we look the more uncertain we become.

To stress the slowness of the changes, it may help to give a scale in which the Earth's age – around 4,600 million years – is represented by one year, so that the time of creation becomes 1 January. The first few months of our scaled-down year will be lifeless, and primitive sea-creatures will not appear until early May. Nothing much more will happen until winter is well advanced; the first fishes date from about 20 November, and the first land creatures are delayed until 30 November. Reptiles will come on the scene on 7 December, and the early mammals on 15 December, but what about Man? The first man-like creatures will not appear until 31 December, at about 5 p.m., and modern men (Homo sapiens) will make their entry at about 11 p.m. on 31 December, so that on the geological timescale we are newcomers. Computer experts may care to take the scale and work out the time when the Battle of Hastings was fought, or the time when Christopher Columbus set out upon his voyage of discovery!

Geologists divide Earth history into definite eras and periods, and can date them with reasonable accuracy, though obviously we cannot be too precise. It may be a help to sum up the 'geological column' in a table:

Period	Beginning (millions of years ago)	End	Notes
PRE-CAMBRIAN			
	4600	590	Few fossils. (The period before 2500 million years ago is often called the Archæan.)
PALEOZOIC (Early)			
Cambrian	590	480	Primitive marine life.
Ordovician	480	435	First fishes.
Silurian	435	405	First land plants.
Devonian	405	340	First amphibians.
Carboniferous	340	260	Luxuriant land vegetation. Coal measures laid down.
Permian	260	225	Reptiles dominant. During the Permian there was a major 'extinction', when many species of plants and animals died out.
MESOZOIC (Middle)			
Triassic	225	180	Great reptiles on land and in the sea. First dinosaurs.
Jurassic	180	130	Age of dinosaurs. Primitive birds; first small mammals.
Cretaceous	130	65	First vegetation of 'modern' type. Trees, toothed birds. At the end of the Cretaceous the dinosaurs vanished.
CENOZOIC (New)			
Eocene	65	55	Rise of mammals; first primates. Flowering plants.
Oligocene	55	38	Large mammals; primates; modern-type birds and plants.
Miocene	38	27	Whales, apes, sabre-toothed cats.
Pliocene	27	2	Modern-type animals.
QUATERNARY (Recent)			
Pleistocene	2	10,000 years	Men. Last Ice Age.
Holocene	10,000 years	Now	Civilization.

There are various other systems of classification. The Carboniferous Period is often divided into the Mississippian (340 to 300 million years ago) and the Pennsylvanian (300 to 260 million years ago), while the Eocene, Oligocene, Miocene and Pliocene are combined into the Tertiary era, but this rough guide will be enough for the moment, so let us see what we can learn from it.

The Pre-Cambrian is poorly understood because of the lack of fossils, but – rather surprisingly – there is evidence that ice ages occurred, or at least spells of relative cold. It is in the Cambrian, which began not far short of 600 million years ago, that we find a great spread of life. There also seems to have been a widespread invasion of the land by the oceans, leading to broad, shallow, warm seas. Trilobites – oval marine life-forms, with many legs – were plentiful in the waters and did not die out until the

end of the Permian.

The Ordovician Period saw a continued spread of marine life, with trilobites still very plentiful; early fishes appeared, and there were periodical advances and retreats of the oceans, together with considerable volcanic activity. At the end of the Ordovician there was another ice age, and this continued into the start of the Silurian, during which the first plants spread on to the lands. During the next period, the Devonian, fishes swarmed in the seas and also in fresh water, while plants developed on the lands – notably ferns, which grew to a great size and formed what may be termed fern-forests. Reddish soil is characteristic of the Devonian, which is named after the county of Devon in the west of England.

We know rather more about the Carboniferous Period, because it was then that the coal deposits were laid

27

This fern forest on Hawaii is little different from those that flourished during the Mesozoic era which ended 65 million years ago.

Below: During the Permian Period, most of the Earth's land masses were combined into one super-continent, now called Pangaea.

down. Giant tree ferns and horse-tails covered the lands; insects such as dragonflies flew around in the primitive forests, and the first amphibians appeared. The world map was very different from that of today. There were several large land-masses, of which the most extensive, in the south, is known as Gondwanaland, while the seas in general were shallow, and at one time there was yet another ice age. Because of the spread of vegetation, the atmosphere was changing, even though it still contained much more carbon dioxide and much less free oxygen than the air we breathe today.

During the last period of the Paleozoic era, the Permian, most of the land-masses were combined into one super-continent, known to geologists as Pangaea. The cold spell which had begun at the end of the Carboniferous soon ended; the trilobites disappeared, and the first reptiles came upon the scene, taking over from the amphibians as the most advanced life-forms on earth. Yet there was an event of tremendous

significance – a great 'extinction', during which around 30 per cent of the plant and animal families disappeared from the face of the world. It was apparently much more severe than the later extinction which involved the death of the dinosaurs.

Next we come to the Mesozoic or middle era, which is divided into three periods: the Triassic, Jurassic and Cretaceous. Altogether it lasted for well over 150 million years, and during this time the super-continent of Pangaea remained more or less intact, though there were minor changes in its form and size. Ferns, horsetails and conifers covered the lands, and amphibians were plentiful, but by now the reptiles had taken over – and the Mesozoic is, above all, the age of the dinosaurs.

Even though the dinosaurs vanished so long ago, they still fascinate us; who has not seen their skeletons in museum collections? Some of them were fearsome indeed. For example, the flesh-eating Tyrannosaurus had a skull over four feet long, and was armed with a set of

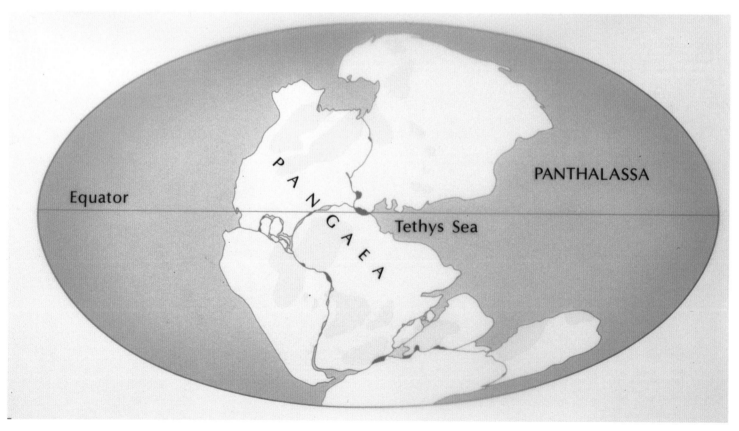

Equator

PANTHALASSA

Tethys Sea

PANGAEA

Death of the dinosaurs. An artist's impression of a pair of Tyrannosaurus Rex succumbing to a global winter triggered by a cometary impact with Earth.

Far right: The Mendenhall Glacier, Junea, Alaska. During the Ice Age, glaciers such as this reached well into the USA and as far south as present-day London, England.

such as Archeopteryx.

Then, quite suddenly, around 65 million years ago – the dinosaurs vanished, and life changed dramatically. Why?

It may simply be that the dinosaurs had reached the limit of their evolution, and were 'worn out'. Alternatively, a minor change in climate might have been enough to doom them; their bodies may have been vast, but their brains were not – and it has been said that no dinosaur was as intelligent as a modern kitten, though this sort of claim is impossible to prove and may be misleading. On the other hand, there is also a very serious suggestion, first made by Luis Alvarez in 1980, that the dinosaurs died as the result of the impact of a large meteorite or asteroid, at least half a dozen miles in diameter. This, said Alvarez, would have produced not only a large crater but also a pall of dust which would have spread all round the world, cutting off the sunlight, so that there was a period when the Earth was a very gloomy place.

The dinosaurs were not the only victims. Many other species of plants and animals died out at the same time, and in fact there was a major 'extinction' similar to that of the earlier Permian Period. But although there is some evidence in favour of Alvarez's theory – notably a surprising amount of the element iridium in rocks dating to the end of the Cretaceous; iridium is often found in meteorites – it is certainly not proved. Other workers believe that the dinosaurs vanished not in a matter of a year or two, but gradually over thousands of years, in which case the collision theory does not fit the facts. We may never know the truth, but from our point of view it is just as well that the dinosaurs departed; only then could mammals develop – and if this had not happened, you and me would not be here.

During the Tertiary era, which began with the death of the dinosaurs and ended a mere two million years ago, life changed slowly into its modern form. Many of the Tertiary mammals have left obvious descendants, though others died out. The small, tree-living primates of the Eocene developed into monkeys and apes; other branches became 'ape-men', and finally we come to *Homo sapiens* or

teeth which would have made short work of most enemies. When 'walking', Tyrannosaurus used only its hind legs – its front legs were too short – and reached a height of almost 6m (20ft). Other flesh-eaters were hardly less impressive, but it is sometimes forgotten that there were also dinosaurs which were harmless and vegetarian. Such were Brontosaurus and Diplodocus, so huge and unwieldy that they seem to have lived most of the time in swamps and would have found moving around on dry land very much of a problem. The largest dinosaur of this kind was Brachiosaurus, which could measure up to 27m (90ft) long from head to tail and weighed around 50,000kg (50 tons). Its front legs were long, and its neck stretched upward, so that if it could be put in a London or New York street it would have no difficulty in poking its head through the window of an office on the third floor. There were some dinosaurs, the Pterodactyls, which could fly, or at least glide; there were Ichthyo-saurs and Plesiosaurs which lived entirely in the sea. All in all, the dinosaurs controlled the entire globe all through the Mesozoic era. They reached their peak during the Jurassic; by the end of the Cretaceous, small mammals had appeared, and there were primitive birds

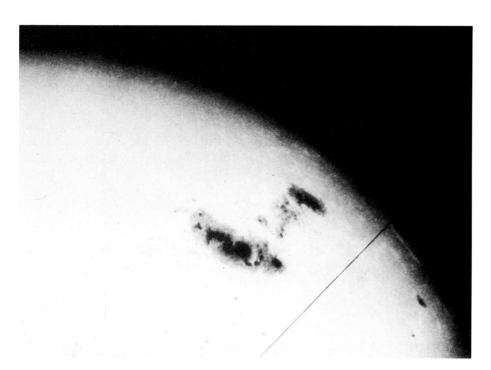

modern man. But the climates were far from constant, and throughout the Pleistocene Period, when Man was becoming dominant, there were periodical cold spells. The Ice Age began about 2,400,000 years ago, and ended only 10,000 years ago. It was not a period of constant low temperature – there were cold spells separated by warmer periods or interglacials – but at the peak of the last glaciation, around 18,000 years ago, the ice-sheets were very extensive indeed. For example, they covered much of the modern United States, and in Britain the edge of the ice extended down to a latitude only slightly north of London.

According to the Jugoslav scientist Milutin Milankovich, the ice ages are produced by slight changes in the Earth's path round the Sun and the changing tilt of its axis of rotation, but there may be other factors too – and we cannot rule out

Above: The sunspots of 1947, the largest ever recorded.

Right: These Alps in the Rhone Valley, France, were thrust up as a result of the gradual northward movement of the African continent against the European continent.

minor variations in the energy sent to us by the Sun. Moreover, we know that the Sun is to some degree a variable star. Every eleven years or so it is very active, exhibiting many of the darker patches we call sunspots; at other times there may be no sunspots at all. Whether or not the amount of solar activity has any direct effect upon our weather is not clear, but certainly there are prolonged warmer and cold periods. Between 1645 and 1715 there were almost no sunspots, so that the regular eleven-year cycle was suspended – and this was an unusually chilly period, sometimes nicknamed the Little Ice Age; in England the Thames froze regularly during the 1680s, and frost fairs were held upon it. Yet there is a marked distinction between short-term 'weather' and longer-term 'climate', and we must keep an open mind. It is even possible that we are now in the midst of an interglacial, in which case the true Ice Age is not over yet.

In 1912 Alfred Wegener, in Germany, published the first of his articles dealing with what is now called the theory of continental drift. Broadly speaking, Wegener suggested that the land masses literally 'float around' over the Earth's interior, and that there are several definite continental 'plates' which can move in relation to each other and may sometimes collide. He pointed out that the present-day continents can be made to fit together; for example, the 'bulge' of South America nearly fits into the 'hollow' of Africa.

For many years Wegener was ignored (possibly because he was a meteorologist rather than a geologist), but since 1960 there has been overwhelming evidence in favour of continental drift, and nobody now doubts that it is correct. We can even trace events far back into the past. About 200 million years ago Pangaea began to break up, and split into two smaller land-masses, Laurasia in the north (including what is now Europe, Asia and most of North America) and Gondwanaland in the south (consisting of modern Australia, Africa, India, Antarctica and South America). Around twenty million years later Gondwanaland itself began to break up; Africa broke away from South America, and India began to drift northward, finally

colliding with Asia around thirty million years ago in an upheaval which led to the birth of the Himalayas. Later, Europe broke away from North America, though Britain was not separated from mainland Europe until the end of the Ice Age.

It all sounds rather like a game of musical chairs, though the rates of drift are very slow – a few inches per year at most, and generally less. Mountains are thrust up where plates collide; one case of this is in mid-Atlantic, where the sea floor is 'spreading' and mountains are being produced – Iceland is simply the top of one of the undersea volcanoes. Plate boundaries are regions where volcanic activity is strong, and there may be violent earthquakes. Where one plate dips below another, and is pushed back into the Earth's interior, we have what is called a trench.

All this shows that the Earth is very far from being a stable, changeless world. No doubt the continental plates will continue to drift around, and in, say, fifty million years' time the world map will look very different from that of today.

Above: Mount Namafjall, near Myvatn in northern Iceland. Known to the locals as The Devil's Kitchen, it is a Dantéesque landscape of bubbling mud pools and sulphurous fumes – a world in the making.

The Earth
as a Planet

Top: The curvature of the Earth, a fact disputed by a few, can clearly be seen in this picture of a cyclone north of Hawaii taken during the Apollo 9 space mission.

Above: An engraving of Ptolemy, the Egyptian astronomer.

Today, when we have explored the whole of the world from pole to pole, it seems rather strange to remember that until only a few centuries ago we did not even know its size. When Christopher Columbus set out on his journey across the Atlantic he believed the Earth to be much smaller than it actually is, which is why he came home without having any real idea of where he had been.

He did at least know that the Earth is a globe. The old idea of a flat Earth, lying motionless in the exact centre of the universe, had been given up long before the time of Christ, and the old Greek philosophers had been able to give definite proofs. For example, the bright southern star Canopus can be seen from Egypt but not from Greece – something which cannot possibly be explained on the flat-earth theory. Also, when the Earth's shadow falls across the Moon during a lunar eclipse we can see that the shadow is curved, showing that the Earth's surface must also be curved.

Of course, not all the ancient peoples agreed. In Hindu teaching the Earth stood on the back of four elephants resting on the shell of a huge tortoise, which was in turn supported by a serpent floating in a boundless ocean; some Indian priests believed that the world was supported on twelve massive pillars – so that during night-time the Sun had to pass underneath the world, somehow or other managing to avoid hitting any of the pillars. To the Egyptians the world was square, with Egypt in the centre, while the sky was formed by the body of a goddess with the rather suitable name of Nut. Believe it or not, there is still an International Flat Earth Society, whose members believe that the Earth is shaped like a pancake, with the North Pole in the middle and a wall of ice all round; pictures taken from high-flying aircraft and artificial satellites are, of course, faked. (I once asked Mr. Samuel Shenton, former President of the Society, what he thought about the South Pole. He replied, with supreme confidence: 'There isn't one!') But the Greeks were much more scientific, and one philosopher – Eratosthenes, who lived from 276 to 196 B.C. – even managed to measure the size of the world with amazing accuracy.

Eratosthenes was in charge of a large library in the city of Alexandria (a library which, alas, no longer exists, to the everlasting regret of historians). From the books there he found that at noon on Midsummer Day the Sun is directly overhead the town of Syene or Assouan, but at this moment the Sun is not overhead Alexandria; it is $7\frac{1}{2}$ degrees away from the zenith or overhead point. A full circle contains 360 degrees, and $7\frac{1}{2}$ is about 1/50 of 360, so that if the Earth is a globe its circumference must be 50 times the distance between Alexandria and Syene. Eratosthenes measured this distance, made some calculations, and finally gave a figure which was very nearly correct. Had Columbus used Era-

tosthenes' value when he set out so many centuries later, he would have known that he could not possibly have reached India.

The next stage was to show that the Earth moves round the Sun rather than being the centre of the universe. Few of the Greeks could bring themselves to believe anything of the kind, but the last great astronomer of Classical times, Ptolemy, used astronomical measurements to make a map of the Mediterranean world which was much better than anything previously drawn, even though he did join Scotland on to England in a sort of back to front position.

Ptolemy died around A.D. 180 and for a long time afterwards there was little progress in any branch of science; from this point of view, the Dark Ages really were dark. It was only in the 16th century that Nicolaus Copernicus, a Polish churchman, sparked off a new revolution in outlook by claiming that the Earth is an ordinary planet moving round the Sun. He was fiercely criticized (not personally, because he was wise enough to hold back publication of his book until he was dying) and the established Church was particularly hostile; in 1600 one philosopher, Giordano Bruno, was burned at the stake in Rome, by order of the Inquisition, for daring to teach that the Earth moves round the Sun (though it is only right to add that this was not his only crime in the eyes of the Church).

Then, in 1610, the great astronomer Galileo turned his first telescope to the sky, and made observations which proved that the old Earth-centred theory could not possibly be correct. Yet it was not until the publication of Isaac Newton's 'Principia', in 1687, that the Earth was finally reduced to the status of a planet. Newton's book, in which he laid down the laws of gravitation, has been the basis of all later work, and has been described as 'the greatest mental effort ever made by one man'.

What we cannot do is to burrow deep into the Earth's globe and find out what happens at great depths. Luckily there are other methods which we can use, and by now we have a reasonably good idea of the structure of the Earth.

The outermost layer is the crust, on which we live. It does not extend downward for very far; represent the Earth by an orange, and the crust will be much less thick than the orange's skin. Below the oceans it has a depth of around 6.5 km (4 miles), and even below the continents its thickness is never more than about 40 km (25 miles). Below it comes the mantle, which accounts for over 80 per cent of the whole volume of the Earth and almost 70 per cent of the total mass; it is made up of magma – that is to say molten rock, mixed in with gas. There is a very sharp

Left: An engraving of Nicolaus Copernicus, the Polish astronomer, who first postulated that the Sun rather than the Earth was at the centre of the Universe.

A modern portrait of Isaac Newton by the English artist Bill Sanderson, which celebrated the 300th anniversary of the publication of Newton's great work, *Philosophiae Naturalis Principia Mathematica*, in 1687.

The shaded areas shown here represent the major earthquake zones of the world, which generally follow continental plate margins. The chief plates of the Earth's crust are marked by colours: Eurasian Plate (yellow), North American Plate (grey), Pacific Plate (blue), Nazca Plate (green), South American Plate (olive), African Plate (orange), Indo-Australian Plate (red), Antarctic Plate (pink).

boundary between the crust and the mantle, known officially as the Mohorovičič Discontinuity after the Jugoslav scientist who first proved its existence, but more commonly as the Moho. The mantle goes down to a depth of 2,900km (1,800 miles), and below it comes the core; the outer core, down to 3,500km (2,200 miles) is liquid, while the inner core, extending to 1,600km (1,000 miles) from the centre of globe, is believed to be solid.

The best way to study the Earth's interior is to make use of earthquakes, which are produced when different plates 'jerk' when passing by each other. Earthquakes can be disastrous, and they have been responsible for many tens of thousands of deaths in modern times, but at least they can tell us a great deal about conditions deep inside the globe.

When an earthquake occurs, waves are set up in the Earth's body. These waves are of various kinds. The P-waves are 'compressional', alternately squeezing and stretching the rocks through which they pass; the S-waves cause a 'shaking' motion, while there are also surface waves which pass round the Earth and cause most of the material damage. The speeds of the P and S waves depend upon the density of the material through which they are passing. For example, there is a

sudden increase in speed as they pass across the Moho, which is how we can find out just where the Moho itself lies.

More importantly, the S waves can pass through liquids, while the P waves cannot. This gives us vital information about the size and position of the liquid part of the Earth's core. What we have to do is to set up recording stations spread widely around the surface, and then measure the effects of the waves reaching them; naturally, we know the position of the epicentre – that is to say, the point on the Earth's surface immediately above the source of the earthquake.

Earthquakes usually happen near the boundaries of the continental plates, so that there are regions which are 'safe' from violent shocks; Britian is one. In places such as Japan, on the other hand, earthquakes are frequent, and cause immense loss of life, as happened in 1923 when a major shock almost destroyed Tokyo. California is another danger zone, particularly near San Francisco, where the San Andreas fault is active; there was a strong earthquake there in 1906, and another in 1989. Unfortunately it seems very likely that there will be a further violent shock there within the next few years, and all that can be done is to make buildings as earthquake-resistant as possible.

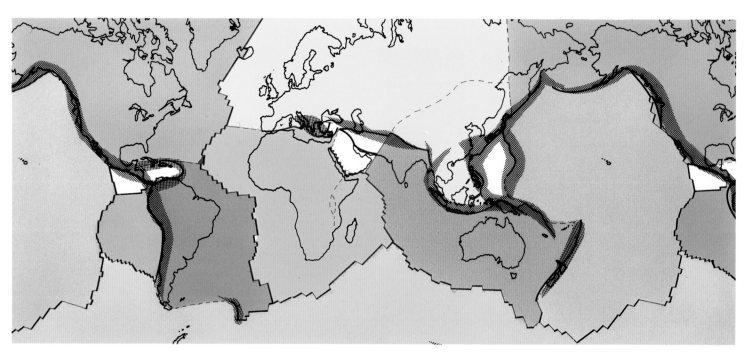

An aerial photograph of the San Andreas Fault, California, as it crosses the Carizzo Plain 450km (300 miles) south of San Francisco.

Studies of earthquake waves show that the Earth's core is very dense, and is presumably made up largely of iron. Iron is, as we know, a good conductor of electricity, and this gives us an explanation for the presence of the Earth's magnetic field.

Electrical currents in conductors are known to produce magnetic fields; this is really the basic principle of the dynamo. Therefore, movements in the iron-rich liquid core can produce a dynamo effect, and the result is a powerful magnetic field with two poles. The north and south magnetic poles are not exactly at the geographical poles, and they shift slowly in position, so that at present the north magnetic pole lies below the Earth's surface in Arctic Canada.

There is evidence that the magnetic field is variable in strength. At the moment it is weakening, and there have even been suggestions that in a few thousands of years it will temporarily disappear, though this is no more than intelligent guesswork and may well be wrong. Most rocks contain particles of magnetic material, and when a rock is formed these particles line up in the direction of the prevailing magnetic field at that time, so that we can look back and see what the magnetic conditions used to be like. Apparently there are periodical 'reversals' when the poles are interchanged for reasons which are not fully understood. The present magnetic field extends well beyond the top of the atmosphere, extending out to some 64,300km (40,000 miles) on the sunward side of the Earth and to over 300,000km (200,000 miles) on the side of the Earth which is turned away from the Sun; the region in which the field is dominant is called the magnetosphere.

The Earth is not unique in having a magnetic field, and in fact the fields of the giant planets are much stronger than ours, particularly in the case of Jupiter.

The magnetosphere is a region surrounding the Earth which contains ionised particles trapped by the Earth's magnetic field. This field interacts with the solar wind, producing a shock front and compressing the magnetosphere. The inner belts of trapped radiation include the Van Allen Belts and regions where auroræ occur.

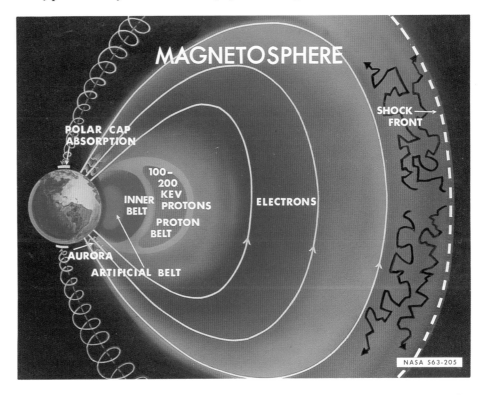

The two outer giants, Uranus and Neptune, have curious magnetic fields, reversed with respect to ours and with their magnetic poles a long way from their poles of rotation. If our field were of that type, we might find that the north magnetic pole lay somewhere in the middle of Australia. On the other hand, Venus seems to have no detectable magnetic field, and that of Mercury is very weak, with Mars regarded as a borderline case.

Next we must turn to volcanoes, most of which lie near the boundaries of the continental plates. They can be spectacular, and highly dangerous, but they are not all alike. Some are violently explosive (such as Vesuvius, which erupted unexpectedly in A.D. 79 and destroyed several towns, including the famous Pompeii), while others are much more predictable.

A volcano arises over a 'hot spot' in the Earth's mantle. Magma forces its way upward, and erupts on to the surface as lava, usually at a temperature of around 1,000°C. When it cools, the lava solidifies as rock. Many volcanoes are crowned by calderas, which are large craters; one, on Mount Aso-san in Japan, has a diameter of over ten miles. Other eruptions occur along fissures, as has happened disastrously in Iceland. Completely new volcanoes are formed now and then; Surtsey, off the Icelandic coast, and Paricutín in Mexico have both come into existence during the past fifty years.

The birth of Paricutín was particularly interesting. On 20 February 1943 a Mexican farmer named Pulido was busy ploughing his cornfield when he came across a small but very deep hole which was sending out gentle wafts of warm vapour. Later in the day the activity increased, and in Pulido's own words: 'At the hole, a fissure had opened, and I noticed that this fissure, as I followed it

The crater of the volcano Vesuvius near Naples. It was this volcano which destroyed Pompeii in A.D. 79. It lies close to the juncture of the African and Eurasian Plates.

with my eye, was long . . . I felt a thunder, the trees trembled, and I saw how, in the hole, the ground swelled and raised itself – six to eight feet high – and a kind of smoke or fine dust, grey like ashes, began to rise up. Immediately there was more smoke, with a hiss and a whistle, loud and continuous, and there was a smell of sulphur . . . Cracks began to appear in the soil, and from below came a terrible noise like the uncorking of a large bottle. Having run for some distance, I looked back and saw a huge column of black smoke roll upward. Then, very frightened, I mounted my horse and rode back to the village.'

Within a few hours the new volcano began to throw out large stones, and during the night lumps of glowing matter were hurled into the air. During 21

February the height increased to over 160m (100 feet), and the first lava began to flow, spreading slowly across the fields. Activity was continuous, and the noise was deafening. Within a week the height had increased to 800m (500ft), and this was more than doubled during the next two months. The luckless villages of Paricutín and Parangaricutiro were buried by the lava, and the whole region changed from a fertile farming area into a blackened waste. Eruptions went on for more than ten years before Paricutín became quiet.

Surtsey was equally unexpected, but did no damage because it rose up from the sea – and has produced an island upon which life has already gained a foothold. Of course, the whole of Iceland is highly volcanic, and large parts of it are

The town of Pompeii was almost completely buried in a short space of time by the eruption of Vesuvius. The town was excavated during the 19th century.

Far right: The edge of the caldera on Santorini in the Mediterranean. A massive eruption of this volcano around 1500 B.C. destroyed the Minoan civilization on the nearby island of Crete.

Below: Kilauea volcano in Hawaii, one of the most active volcanoes in the world.

lava-covered.

Because the Earth's plates are constantly moving, a volcano will not remain over the hot spot indefinitely. The islands of Hawaii provide good examples of what happens. There is a whole chain of volcanoes, of which the two highest are Mauna Kea and Mauna Loa on Big Island, both of which rise to around 22,530m (14,000ft). Mauna Kea is extinct, because it has moved away from the hot spot; it has not erupted for thousands of years, and will probably never do so again (at least, we hope not, because one of the world's greatest astronomical observatories has been set up at its summit). Mauna Loa, on the other hand, can be very active indeed, produc-

ing streams of lava which pour out at high velocity. On one occasion the lava spread as far as the outskirts of Hilo, the only large town on Big Island – and according to local legend, was halted only by the spells cast by a powerful witch-doctor who had been hastily called in by the authorities! Kilauea, adjoining Mauna Loa, is also very violent; on its floor is a lava-lake known as Halemaumau, or the 'House of Eternal Fire', which was said to be the home of the ferocious fire-goddess Pele. Halemaumau is active for most of the time, and can produce spectacular 'firework displays', though on the occasions when I have been there it has stubbornly refused to perform.

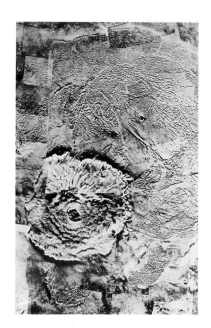

Above: Olympus Mons, the most spectacular shield volcano in the Solar System. It rises some 25km (15 miles) above the surrounding plains and is more than 700km (430 miles) in diameter. The central caldera is over 80km (50 miles) across.

All British volcanoes have been extinct for a very long time, but there are a number in the Mediterranean area apart from the famous Italian volcanoes such as Vesuvius, Etna and Stromboli. There was a major eruption around 1500 B.C. on Thira (Santorini) in the Greek islands. Following an eruption, the top of the volcano collapsed; sea poured in, and the result was a tremendous explosion, producing gigantic waves which swept across the sea and hit the coast of the island of Crete, more or less wiping out the highly advanced civilization which had arisen there (and, incidentally, giving rise to the legend of the lost continent of Atlantis). Go to Thira today, and you will see the old caldera. It is now quiet, though there are areas where smoke issues from the ground, and now and then there are strong earthquakes.

A much later eruption of the same type was in 1883, when the island of Krakatoa, between Java and Sumatra, blew up. Huge waves swamped the coast of Java, and thousands of lives were lost, while the dust and ash thrown into the upper air remained there for years, producing strange-coloured sunsets. In recent times, too, many people will remember the eruption of Mount St. Helens in the State of Washington, which destroyed the beautiful shape of the volcano and reduced the area to a wasteland.

Volcanoes are found on other planets. On Mars we find many, one of which, Mount Olympus (Olympus Mons) is three times the height of Everest, and is topped by a 40-mile caldera. The Martian volcanoes may be extinct, but there is almost certainly a great deal of present-day vulcanism on Venus, and radar measurements have enabled us to track down at least two large shield volcanoes, Rhea Mons and the Theia Mons. Certainly there is constant volcanic activity on Io, one of Jupiter's large satellites, though admittedly the volcanoes there are different from ours, and the Ionian surface is red and sulphur-coated.

All we have found out about the Earth shows us that although it is only one of the Sun's family of planets, it is exceptional in some respects. In particular, it alone has broad oceans of water, and it alone has air which we can breathe.

Right: A column of ash, hot gases and pulverised rock shooting out of Mount St. Helens volcano, Washington State, USA, during an eruption on 22 July 1980, two months after the major eruption which removed much of one side of the volcano and destroyed thousands of square miles of surrounding countryside.

The Atmosphere and Beyond

We live at the bottom of an ocean of air. Without it we could not exist, and no life could have appeared on the Earth. It is fortunate for us that our world is of just the right mass and is at just the right temperature to produce an atmosphere which suits us.

Everything depends upon escape velocity, which is the speed needed to break free from an attracting body without using extra power. Throw an object upward, and it will rise to a certain height and then fall back; the faster you throw it up, the higher it will go before returning. If you could throw it up at a speed of 11.2 km/sec (7 miles/sec) it would never come down at all, because the Earth's pull would not be strong enough to draw it back, and it would move out into space. This is why 11.2km/sec is known as the Earth's escape velocity.

The atmosphere is made up of millions upon millions of atoms and molecules, all moving about quickly. If an air-particle could work up to 11.2km/sec, it could break free. Fortunately this cannot happen, because the particles making up our air cannot achieve such a speed, but – as we have seen – things are very different on the Moon, where the escape velocity is a mere 2.4km/sec (1.5 miles/sec). Any atmosphere that the Moon may once have had has long since leaked away into space. On the other hand the giant planets, with their high escape velocities – 60km/sec (37 miles/sec) in the case of Jupiter – can hold down even very light gases, which is why they contain so much hydrogen and helium.

Most of the Earth's air is made up of two gases, nitrogen (78 per cent) and oxygen (21 per cent), with much smaller amounts of other gases such as argon and carbon dioxide, and of course a considerable but variable amount of water vapour. No other planet in the Solar System has an atmosphere like ours. Titan, the largest of Saturn's family of moons, has a dense atmosphere made up largely of nitrogen, but most of the rest is methane, which is a compound of carbon and hydrogen, so that from our point of view it would be quite unbreathable – quite apart from the fact that Titan is a very cold world indeed.

The bottom part of our air is known as the troposphere. It stretches upward for about 8km (5 miles) to 18km (11 miles), according to latitude (it is deepest over the equator) and it is here that we find all our usual 'weather', together with all

A section through the atmosphere, showing its main layers.

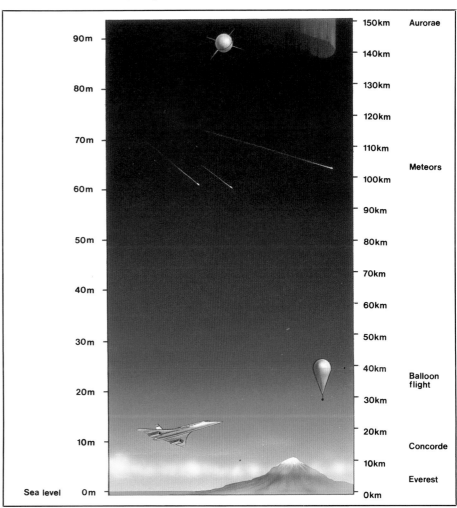

90m	150km — Aurorae
	140km
80m	130km
	120km
70m	110km
	100km — Meteors
60m	90km
50m	80km
	70km
40m	60km
30m	50km
	40km — Balloon flight
20m	30km
10m	20km
	10km — Concorde
Sea level 0m	Everest 0km

Above: Some cellular-type clouds over the Atlantic Ocean northwest of the Cape Verde Islands. The photograph was taken by one of the crew members of the Space Shuttle *Challenger* in 1984.

normal clouds. The temperature drops with increasing height, and at the top of the troposphere it has fallen to about −80 degrees Fahrenheit. The density also drops, as every climber knows; go to the top of Everest, and you will need an oxygen mask, while all high-flying aircraft have to be equipped with pressurized cabins.

Above the tropopause, which marks the top of the troposphere, we come to a much more rarefied region known as the stratosphere, which extends up to 48km (30 miles) or so. Strangely enough, the temperature in the stratosphere does not go on decreasing, and indeed it rises, reaching 60 degrees Fahrenheit near the top. This is because of the presence of a layer of ozone, which is a special form of oxygen; its chemical formula is O_3, indicating that an ozone molecule is made up of three atoms of oxygen instead of the usual two. Short-wave radiation from the Sun warms the ozone layer and prevents the temperature from falling.

Note, however, that this does not make the stratosphere 'hot'. Scientifically, temperature is defined by the rate at which the various atoms and molecules move around: the faster the motions, the higher the temperature. The particles in the stratosphere are quick-moving, but there are so few of them that there is virtually no 'heat'. The best example I can give is to compare a red-hot poker with a firework sparkler. Each spark is at a very high temperature, but contains so little mass that the firework can safely be hand-held – though I for one would not be in the least inclined to grasp the end of a glowing poker!

Above the stratosphere there are other regions with a rather confused system of nomenclature. We have the mesosphere (up to 80km (50 miles)) and then the thermosphere (up to 290km (180 miles)); the temperature of the mesosphere is low, but in the thermosphere it rises to well over 3,500 degrees Fahrenheit, though at this height the density of the air is very low indeed. We also find layers which reflect some kinds of radio waves, and make long-range communication possible. Because the layers contain ions, or incomplete atoms, the region is usually termed the ionosphere.

From 480km (300 miles) we come to the outermost part of the air, known as the exosphere. It has no definite boundary, and simply thins out until it can no longer be detected. Broadly speaking, it is fair to say that above a height of 800km (500 miles) there is no atmosphere left.

Ozone is of vital importance to us, because it blocks out harmful short-wave radiations coming from space. If this did not happen, life on Earth would be impossible. In recent years we have heard a great deal about 'holes' in the ozone layer, and it has been suggested that these are due to chemical substances which we release into the atmosphere – and which attack and destroy the ozone molecules. As yet there is no definite proof that we are responsible, but certainly the whole situation will have to be very carefully watched.

We also have to reckon with cosmic rays, which are not rays at all, but high speed atomic particles bombarding the Earth from all directions all the time. Luckily for us they are broken up in the stratosphere, and only their shattered fragments reach the ground. I say 'luckily' because the original 'primary' cosmic rays would produce another hazard to life on Earth – something which we will have to bear in mind when we set up permanent bases on the Moon, where there is no atmospheric shield.

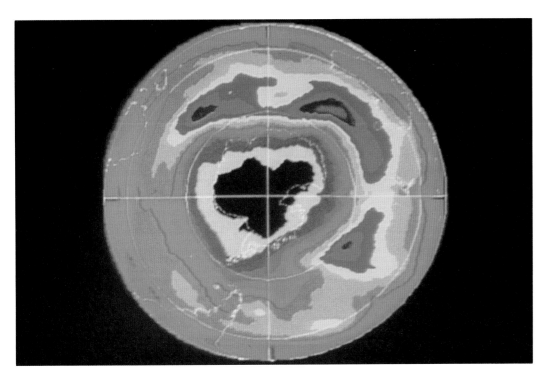

I have already mentioned meteors, which are cometary débris. They are quite harmless, and are usually smaller than grains of sand. They become luminous when they dash into the air at heights of around 190km (120 miles) above the ground, and they burn away before they have penetrated below 65km (40 miles), ending their journey in the form of very fine 'dust'. What we see as a shooting-star is not the tiny particle itself, but the effects which it produces as it plunges through the air at an initial speed which may be as great as 70km/sec (45miles/sec). There may be a connection between meteors and the strange, lovely noctilucent clouds, which are to be found in the mesosphere and are quite different from our normal clouds even though they are presumably made up of ice-crystals.

When radio was developed, it was at first thought that there would be no chance of sending messages across great distances from one part of the Earth's surface to another, simply because radio waves travel in straight lines and would be expected to go outward into space. When this proved to be incorrect, some explanation had to be found – and this led on to the discovery of the layers in the ionosphere which reflect some radio waves back to the ground. These layers lie at heights of between 80 and 320km (50–200 miles), and are somewhat variable; in particular, they are affected by activity taking place in the Sun.

Well above the stratosphere we meet with the beautiful auroræ, or polar lights – Aurora Borealis in the nothern hemisphere, Aurora Australis in the southern. Auroræ are due to electrified particles sent out by the Sun, which cascade down into the upper air and make it glow. Because the particles are charged, they tend to spiral down toward the magnetic

The X-15 research plane used by NASA in the late 1950s and early '60s to explore the limits of speed and altitude by a rocket-powered plane. A variant of this, the X-15A-2, achieved a speed of 6,850km/h (4,250 mph) in 1966. Altitudes in excess of 50 miles were regularly reached.

poles, which are why auroræ are best seen from high latitudes. From places such as North Norway and North Canada they are visible on almost any clear night, and they are common enough over most of Scotland, but from South England they are rare, and from regions near the equator they are hardly ever to be seen (though it is on record that an aurora was once visible from Singapore!). Naturally, auroræ are commonest when the Sun is near the peak of its eleven-year cycle of activity. For example, there was a superb display on 13 March 1989 as seen from England, and was bright enough to cast shadows. It was not entirely unexpected, and was associated with a very large sunspot group on the solar face.

Auroræ may take various forms: glows, rays, arcs, bands, curtains and streamers, often vividly coloured and changing very quickly. Because they are

so high, ranging from 96–960km (60–600 miles), they could not be expected to produce any noise – and yet it has been claimed that hisses and crackles have been heard during brilliant displays. Whether or not these reports are reliable must be regarded as dubious, and certainly 'auroral noise' would be very hard to explain. Pungent odours have also been claimed, though I admit that I have absolutely no faith in the reality of smelly auroræ!

Do not confuse auroræ with the Zodiacal Light, a cone-shaped glow which can sometimes be seen rising up from the horizon below which the Sun has set or from which it is about to rise. The Zodiacal Light is caused by sunlight shining upon the thinly-spread matter in the main plane of the Solar System.

Aircraft can fly at tens of thousands of feet, and balloons carrying scientific equipment can go even higher, but if we want to explore the upper part of the atmosphere and regions beyond we have to use space research methods – that is to say, rocket power. Rockets, unlike conventional flying machines, do not depend upon the presence of atmosphere, because they work according to what Isaac Newton called the principle of reaction: every action has an equal and opposite reaction.

Consider a firework rocket of the type fired by Britons on Guy Fawkes' Night (5 November) or by Americans on Independence Day (4 July). A rocket of this sort is made up of a hollow tube filled with gunpowder. When you 'light the blue touch-paper and retire immediately' the gunpowder starts to burn, and gives off hot gas. The gas tries to escape from the tube, but can do so in only one direction – through the exhaust, where the touch-paper has been burned away. Therefore, the gas rushes out of the exhaust in a concentrated stream, and as it does so it 'kicks' the rocket in the opposite direction. So long as the gas keeps on streaming out, the rocket will continue to fly. The atmosphere through which it flies is actually a nuisance, because it sets up friction.

The first rockets were made many centuries ago, and the Chinese used them for elaborate displays, but the first serious idea of sending them into space was proposed by a Russian, Konstantin Eduardovich Tsiolkovskii, who published a series of papers about them almost a hundred years ago. Tsiolkovskii was purely a theorist, and never actually fired a rocket in his life, but some of his suggestions were remarkably 'modern', and he is rightly regarded as the true founder of space-travel.

Tsiolkovskii realized that solid fuels, such as gunpowder, are too weak and too uncontrollable to be used for long journeys in space, and so he proposed to use liquid propellants. What is done is to take two different liquids and combine them in a combustion chamber, where they react together and produce gas which is sent out from the exhaust as with the firework. Tsiolkovskii also knew that to break free from the Earth without using any extra power means working up to escape velocity and that this is best done by mounting rockets one on top of the

other, so that the upper vehicle is given what may be called a running start before it has to fire its own motors. This is the principle of the step-launcher which has been used to send men to the Moon and probes out to all the main planets of the Solar System.

The first liquid-propellant rocket was fired in 1926 by the American pioneer Robert Hutchings Goddard, and though it covered no more than 320 m (220ft), travelling at a maximum speed of 96km/hr (60m.p.h.), it showed that the basic principles were sound. Some years later a German amateur group, including Wernher von Braun, set up a testing ground outside Berlin and produced rockets which were at least promising even if many of them either exploded on the ground or else took off in the wrong direction. Unfortunately the Nazi Government realized that the rocket could be used as a weapon of war, so the Berlin group was closed down and its leading members transferred to Peenemünde, an island in the Baltic, to produce military rockets. It was here that von Braun's team produced the V.2 weapons which bombarded South England during the late stages of the war.

Below: The world's first liquid-fuelled rocket was launched by Robert Goddard in Massachusetts in 1926.

A diagram showing the relative sizes of various launch vehicles. *Upper row, left to right:* A-1 Sputnik, Scout, V2. *Bottom row, left to right:* Saturn V, D-1 Salyut, Space Shuttle, Ariane 1.

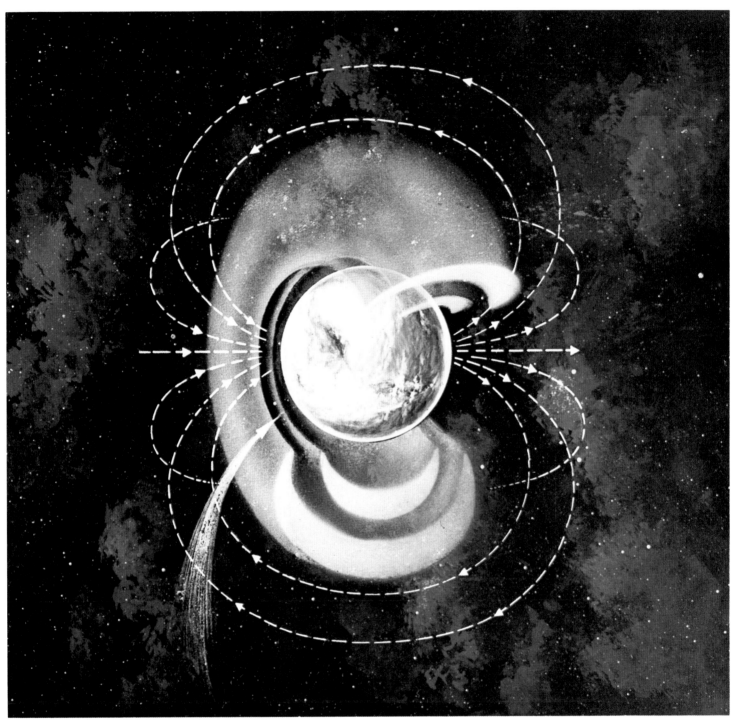

Subsequently von Braun and others went to America to carry out more peaceful experiments, and before long they were able to send rockets up to dizzy heights of more than 320km (200 miles),

Yet the first real triumph came not from the United States, but from the USSR. On 4 October 1957 the Russians opened the true Space Age when they launched Sputnik 1, the first of all man-made moons or artificial satellites. It was no larger than a football, and it carried nothing apart from a radio transmitter, but it was immensely significant.

If an artificial satellite is taken up by rocket and put into a closed path round

The diagram above shows the relationship between the Earth's magnetic field (dotted lines) and the Van Allen Belts (the doughnut-shaped rings). The path taken by incoming cosmic rays is also shown.

49

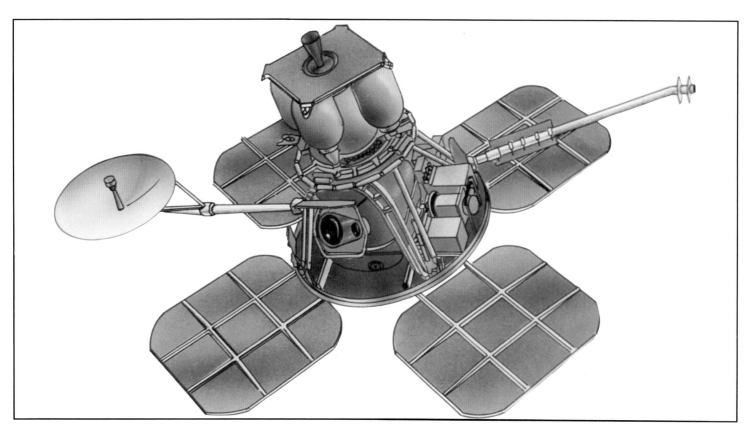

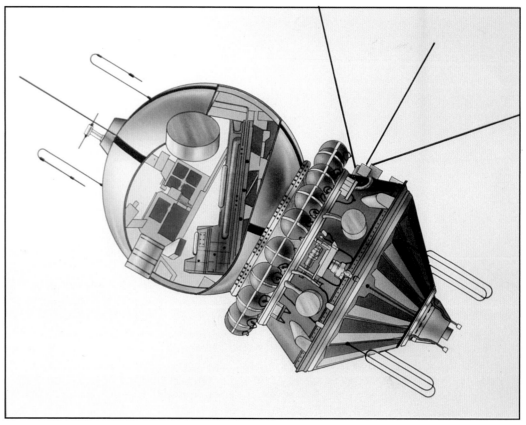

Above: One of the five Lunar Orbiters which were placed in orbit around the Moon at three-monthly intervals, beginning in August 1966. Their task was to return detailed TV pictures of the whole of the lunar surface, which they did with great success.

Right: The Russian Vostok craft were used to launch the first humans into space. The first prototype, Sputnik 4, was launched in May 1960. Vostok 1 took Yuri Gagarin into space on 12 April 1961.

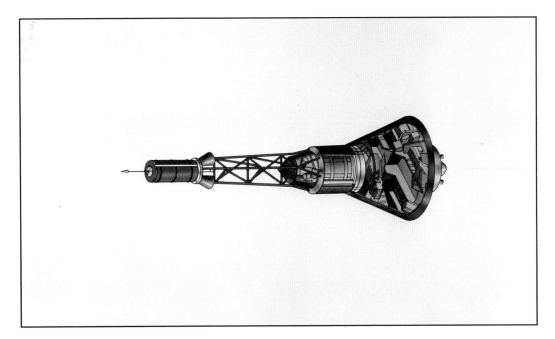

the Earth, it will not fall down any more than the real Moon will do. Provided that it stays above the top of the resisting part of the atmosphere, it will behave in exactly the same way as a natural astromomical body. Sputnik I was not sufficiently high to be permanent, and came down in the first week of 1958, because it had to force its way through the tenuous upper air and was 'braked' by friction, so that it dropped back into the dense lower atmosphere and burned away. But before long other artificial satellites were launched, and the first of the American vehicles, Explorer I – master-minded by von Braun – made a vitally important discovery.

Explorer I was launched on 1 February 1958, and was put into an elliptical path which carried it from 360 to 2550 km (225–1580 miles) above the ground, with an orbital period of 115 minutes. It was only 14kg (31lb) in weight, but it carried a Geiger counter, which is an instrument used to study charged particles and high-energy radiation, with the intention of counting the numbers of cosmic ray particles at various heights. To everyone's surprise, the cosmic ray counts stopped suddenly when Explorer reached a height of 965km (600 miles) – and this happened every time that the satellite went through the 'critical height'.

The situation was most peculiar, and at first the American team headed by James Van Allen simply did not know what to make of it. It was absurd to suppose that the region above 965km (600 miles) was free from cosmic rays, and there had to be another explanation. Before long, Van Allen realized the truth. There were so many particles that the Geiger counters in Explorer could not cope with them, and had become jammed. In fact, the Earth is circled by a zone of high-energy radiation.

Later it was found that there are two zones, an inner one made up chiefly of protons (the positively-charged nuclei of atoms) and an outer one consisting mainly of electrons (the negatively-charged parts of atoms). Today these Van Allen Zones are known to be of tremendous significance. They are strongly affected by what is termed the solar wind, which consists of electrified particles sent out by the Sun. When the Van Allen Zones are overloaded by the solar wind, particles cascade downward to produce displays of auroræ.

Since those early days, satellites of all kinds have been sent up, many of them in orbits so high that they will never come down. Life today would seem strange without them – to give just one example, satellites make long-range television coverage possible, which is why you can tune in your set and watch a game of cricket or baseball being played on the

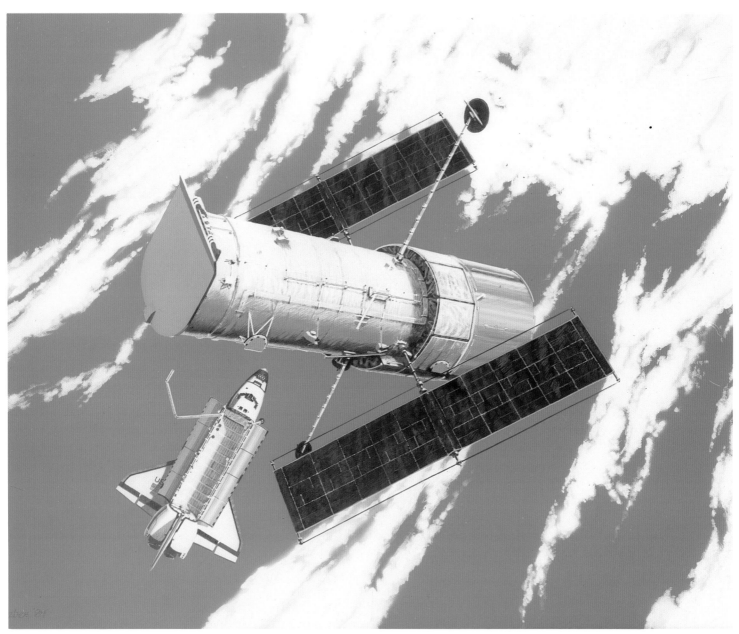

An artist's impression of the Hubble Space Telescope being delivered into orbit by the Space Shuttle.

other side of the world. They have been of the utmost use to astronomers, physicists, chemists and biologists, and dozens of astronauts have been into space since the first flight, by Yuri Gagarin in 1961. The latest triumph has been the launch of the Hubble Space Telescope in April 1990.

So far as the Earth itself is concerned, it is worth noting that satellites make it possible to study whole weather systems, giving us a greatly improved knowledge of the atmosphere as a whole; photographs of the surface taken at various

wavelengths are invaluable to geologists; we can examine wide areas to detect places where the vegetation is diseased; we can study the poles and other areas difficult to reach from the ground – in fact, there is no end to the uses of artificial satellites in studying the Earth. It is true, unfortunately, that space vehicles and artificial satellites can also be turned into military weapons, and we can only hope that 'star wars' will never become reality. We would be wise to take good care of the Earth; we have nowhere else to go.

The Earth's Moon

The world would seem a strange place without our Moon. For part of every month it shines down brilliantly from the night sky, and it was natural for ancient peoples to worship it as a god – or at least as the home of a god. Lunar cults were not always gentle; for example, the Aleutian Islanders were in the habit of stoning to death anyone who dared to offend the Moon!

There are plenty of legends, too, many of which concern the Old Man in the Moon, whose outline is said to be indicated by the dark patches on the lunar disk. One German tale tells how the Old Man was a villager who was thrown on to the Moon after he was caught stealing cabbages. In a Polynesian legend, a girl named Sina made the unfortunate remark that the Moon looked like a large breadfruit, with the result that the angry Moon swooped down and captured both Sina and her child. To the Greenlanders the Sun and Moon were brother and sister, and after a quarrel the Sun rubbed soot in his sister's face; the Moon set out in pursuit, and still follows him across the sky, but she can never catch him, because she cannot fly high enough.

My favourite lunar myth comes from China. It is said that there was once a great drought, and a herd of elephants

Left: An outstanding view of the full Moon, taken at 10,000 nautical miles from the Apollo spacecraft on its homeward journey.

Below: An illustration by Sally Bensusen of The Man in the Moon (1988).

The Phases of the Moon (for an explanation refer to the text on page 55).

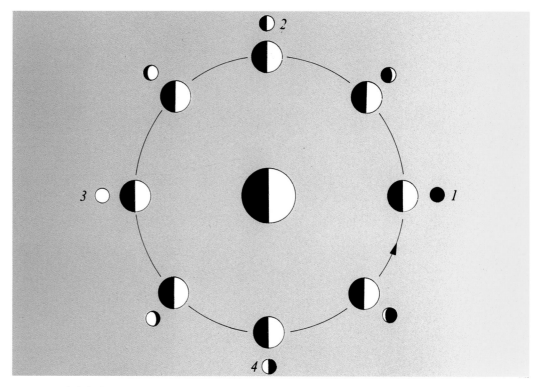

came to drink from a sheet of water called the Moon Lake. They trod on so many of the local hares that when they next appeared, an intelligent hare pointed out that they were annoying the Moon-goddess by disturbing her reflection in the water. The elephants agreed that this was most unwise, and hastily departed, never to return!

Ancient astronomers did their best to find out something quite definite about the Moon itself. One of the early Greeks, Anaximander, believed that the Moon was 'a circle nineteen times as large as the Earth; it is shaped like a chariot-wheel, the rim of which is hollow and full of fire', while Xenophanes, who died in 478 B.C. at the advanced age of 100, held that the Sun, Moon and stars were clouds which had been set alight in some manner. But the later Greeks had ideas which were much more advanced, and one of them, Aristarchus, even made a very reasonable estimate of the Moon's distance from the Earth. Aristarchus also believed that the Earth moves round the Sun, so that he anticipated Copernicus by more than 1800 years. And around A.D. 80 the Roman writer Plutarch wrote an essay, *On the Face in the Orb of the Moon*, in which he claimed that the

Moon was 'earthy', with mountains and valleys.

In those times there seemed to be no definite reason why the Moon should not be inhabited. One of the first science-fiction novels about lunar travel was written in the second century A.D. by a Greek named Lucian, who called it the *True History* because, as he was careful to explain, it contained nothing but lies from beginning to end. It was never meant to be taken seriously, and his method of sending his travellers moonward was unusual: a party of sailors, caught up in a waterspout while passing through the Straits of Gibraltar, were hurled upward for seven days and seven nights until they finally landed on the Moon. On arrival, they become involved in a battle between the King of the Moon and the King of the Sun, who had quarrelled over their rival claims to colonizing the planet Venus. The opposing armies included three-headed birds, flea-riders, horse-vultures and spiders as large as islands. . . . It was only after the invention of the telescope, in the seventeenth century, that the airless, lifeless nature of the Moon was finally proved.

Everyone must be familiar with the lunar phases, or apparent changes in shape of the Moon from new to full. Because the Moon has no light of its own, half of it is sunlit while the other half is not, and the phases depend upon how much of the 'day' side is turned toward us. In the diagram – which is not to scale – the Moon is shown in four positions. At 1, the dark side is turned toward us, and the Moon cannot be seen at all; this, not the thin crescent visible later in the evening sky, is the true new moon. As the Moon moves along a little of the day side begins to be turned in our direction, and by the time it has reached position 2 the phase is 'half'; this is known as First Quarter, because the Moon has then completed one quarter of its orbit. Between positions 2 and 3 the Moon is gibbous (more than half, less than full) and at 3 the whole of the sunlit face is turned toward us. Then the phases are repeated in the reverse order: gibbous, half again (position 4, Last Quarter) and back to new.

When the Moon is in its crescent stage, the 'night' side can often be seen shining faintly. There is no mystery about this; it is due to light reflected on to the Moon from the Earth, so that it is known as the Earthshine.

The Moon takes 27.3 days to complete one orbit, but we must remember that both it and the Earth are moving round the Sun, so that the interval between one new moon and the next – the so-called synodic period – is not 27.3 days, but 29.5 days.

The Moon's distance from the Earth ranges between 356,395km (221,460 miles) at its closest (perigee) out to 406,766km (252,760 miles) at its furthest (apogee), giving a mean of 384,365km (238,840 miles). By a curious coincidence – it can be nothing more – the Moon and the Sun look almost exactly the same size in our sky; the Sun has a diameter four hundred times greater than that of the Moon, but it is also four hundred times further away. This means that if the lining-up at new moon is exact, the Moon can just cover the brilliant solar disk, producing a total eclipse. Eclipses do not happen every month, because the Moon's orbit is tilted at an angle of just over five degrees, and on most occasions the new moon passes unseen either above or below the Sun in

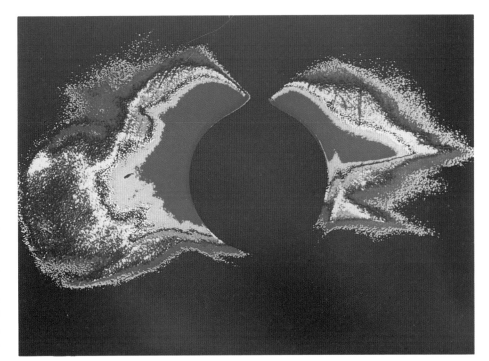

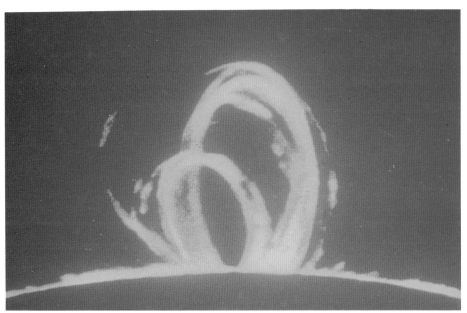

the sky. This is a pity, because a total eclipse is without doubt the most glorious sight in all nature. As soon as the brilliant face is hidden the Sun's atmosphere flashes into view, and we see the glorious pearly 'corona' stretching outward, together with masses of red hydrogen gas which are known as prominences; the sky darkens, and planets and bright stars can be seen. No total eclipse can last for longer than eight minutes,

Above: A spectacular solar prominence. The outbursts follow magnetic field lines.

Top: The Sun's outer atmosphere, or corona, colour-coded to distinguish levels of brightness, reaches outwards for millions of miles. The photograph was taken from Skylab.

55

A total eclipse of the Moon. Total blackness is never achieved and the resulting colour is due to the Earth's atmosphere.

eruption. For example, the eclipse of 1884, not long after the Krakatoa outbreak, was very dark indeed.

Eclipses of the Moon may be either total or partial. Unlike solar eclipses they are leisurely affairs, and totality may last for as long as 1 hour 44 minutes. It cannot honestly be said that lunar eclipses are important, but they are always well worth watching. The next total eclipses will be those of 9 December 1992, 4 July 1993, 29 November 1993 and 4 April 1996 – and when a lunar eclipse occurs, it can be seen from any part of the Earth from which the Moon is above the horizon at the time.

It so happens that the Earth, Sun and Moon return to almost the same relative positions every 18 years $10\frac{1}{4}$ days (a period known as the Saros), so that any eclipse is apt to be followed by another eclipse 18 years $10\frac{1}{4}$ days later. The agreement is not exact, but it is at least reasonable, and it means that eclipses could be predicted even in ancient times.

There are various true stories associated with eclipses. One of these concerns Christopher Columbus. During his famous voyage his ship was at one time anchored off Jamaica, and problems arose when the natives refused to send him any food. Columbus told them that unless they mended their ways he would make the Moon 'change her colour, and lose her light'. He knew that an eclipse was due – and when it started, the Jamaicans were so alarmed that they promptly raised Columbus to the status of a god, and sent him all the supplies he needed!

It is not strictly accurate to say simply that the Moon moves round the Earth. More properly, the two move together round their common centre of gravity, which is called the barycentre. This is how the two bells of a dumb-bell will behave if you twist them by the bar joining them, but there is one important difference: because the two bells will be equal in weight, the centre of gravity or 'balancing point' will be in the middle of the bar. But the Earth is 81 times as massive as the Moon, so that the balancing point is displaced; in fact the barycentre lies inside the Earth's globe, about 1,705km (1,060 miles) below the surface. I admit, however, that the usual state-

and most are much shorter; unless the Sun is completely covered, the corona and the prominences cannot be seen. The last total eclipse to be seen from England was that of 1927, and the next will not be until 11 August 1999, but if you do not want to wait for as long as that you may care to plan a visit to Mexico or Brazil on 11 July 1991, the South Atlantic on 30 June 1992, or Peru or Brazil again on 3 November 1994.

A lunar eclipse is different, and is obviously not due to anything blotting the Moon out, because the Moon is the closest natural body in the sky. If the lining-up is exact when the Moon is full (position 3), the Moon passes into the shadow cast by the Earth, and the supply of direct sunlight is cut off, so that the disk turns a dim, often coppery colour until the Moon emerges from the shadow. At most eclipses the Moon does not disappear completely, because some of the Sun's rays are bent or refracted on to it by way of the ring of atmosphere round the Earth, but some eclipses are much 'darker' than others – particularly when there is a great deal of dust in the Earth's upper air following a major volcanic ment that 'the Moon goes round the Earth' is good enough for most purposes.

The Earth spins on its axis once in 24 hours, but the Moon takes much longer; its rotation period is 27.3 days – exactly the same as its orbital period. This is why the same face is turned toward us all the time. To show what is meant, walk round a chair, turning as you go so as to keep your face turned chairward all the time. Anyone sitting on the chair will never see the back of your neck – and sitting on the Earth, we never see the 'back' of the Moon. Before the Russians sent a rocket probe on a round trip, in 1959, we had no definite knowledge of what it was like, even though our ideas proved to be very near the reality.

Note that although the Moon keeeps the same face turned toward the Earth, it does not keep the same face turned toward the Sun, so that day and night conditions are the same all over Moon – apart from the fact that from the far side, the Earth can never be seen. Once the Sun rises over the lunar landscape, it does not set again for a period almost as long as two Earth weeks.

There is no mystery about this apparently curious behaviour, and it is not pure coincidence. In its early history the Moon was closer to the Earth than it is now, and rotated much more rapidly. It was not firm and solid, so that the Earth's pull raised strong tides in it, tending to keep a 'bulge' turned earthward. The result was that the spin was slowed down, rather as a cycle wheel will slow down when it is spinning between two brake shoes. Eventually the rotation had stopped altogether relative to the Earth, and this is the state of affairs today. All the other major satellites of the planets have similarly 'captured' or synchronous rotations. For example, Titan takes 15 days 23 hours to complete one orbit round Saturn – and also 15 days 23 hours to make one full rotation on its axis.

Though the Moon spins at a constant speed, it does not move in its orbit at a constant speed; following the usual traffic laws of the Solar System, it moves fastest when closest to us (perigee) and slowest when farthest away (apogee). This means that during every month the position in orbit and the amount of axial spin become out of step, and the Moon

seems to rock very slowly to and fro; first we can see a little way round one edge, and then a little way around the other. This is termed 'libration in longitude'. There is also a 'libration in latitude', because the Moon's path is appreciably tilted, and finally a 'diurnal libration', because we are observing from the surface of the Earth rather than its centre. The result of all these librations is that we can examine a grand total of 59 per cent of the Moon's surface, though never more than 50 per cent at any one moment. Only 41 per cent is permanently out of view, though the edge or libration regions are so foreshortened that they are very difficult to map.

Everyone knows that the Moon rises in an easterly direction and sets toward the west. This due to the real rotation of the Earth on its axis, from west to east. The Moon is also moving in its orbit from west to east, and so it seems to travel eastward against the stars by about 13 degrees per day (remember that the apparent diameter of the full moon is about half a degree). The apparent path of the Moon in the sky is not very different from that of the Sun, which is termed the ecliptic. When full, the Moon is opposite to the Sun in the sky, and so to observers in the northern hemisphere of the Earth it lies due south at midnight.

A diagram illustrating libration in longitude. See the text for a full explanation.

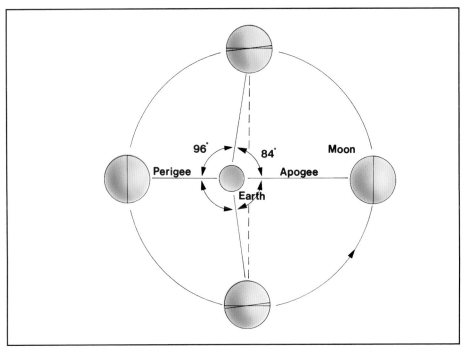

Right; Diagram illustrating the angle of the ecliptic (see the text below for explanation).

Below: The Harvest Moon.

In the next diagram, the angle of the ecliptic against the horizon is shown for March and September. In March, the angle is at its steepest. In 24 hours the Moon moves from position 1 to position 2, and obviously the difference in rising-time between one night and the next – the 'retardation' is marked. In September the angle is much shallower, and although the Moon moves against the stars by the same amount – in other words, the distance between 1 and 2 is the same in each section of the diagram – the retardation will be less. It may be as little as a quarter of an hour, no matter where you are on the Earth's surface.

It is often said that in September the full moon rises at the same time on several evenings in succession. This is not true, and the retardation is always appreciable, but it is much less than at other times of the year. The September full moon is called the Harvest Moon, because farmers used to find it useful as an extra source of light at a particularly busy time; the following full moon is called Hunter's Moon.

It has often been said that the Harvest Moon looks larger than usual, but this is quite wrong – and it is also wrong to say that the full moon looks larger when low over the horizon than it does when high in the sky. This is the celebrated Moon Illusion. It has been known for centuries, but it *is* an illusion and nothing more, as you will find out if you measure it.

Finally, I must make a brief mention of occultations. As the Moon moves across the sky it may sometimes pass in front of a star, and hide or occult it. Because a star is to all intents and purposes a point source of light, and the Moon has no air, the occulation is sudden; the star shines steadily until the moment when it is covered by the advancing Moon, when it snaps out abruptly. If there were any lunar atmosphere, the star would flicker and fade for several seconds before vanishing – and this was one of the earliest proofs that the Moon is airless. Next time there is an occultation of a bright star, watch it if you can; I assure you that it can be quite startling.

The Moon
and the Earth

Earthrise over the Moon.

Because the Moon is so close to us, it affects the Earth more than any other body in the sky, with the obvious exception of the Sun. In particular, it is the main cause of the ocean tides.

Many people are confused about the tides, and it is quite true that the whole theory is very complicated indeed, so that for the moment I propose to simplify it as much as possible. First, then let us imagine that the whole of the Earth is covered with a shallow ocean, and that both the Earth and the Moon are motionless. In the diagram, we have a high tide at A and another high tide at B. The tide at A is straightforward enough, because the Moon's gravitational pull is heaping up the water (it is heaping up the land, too, but to a much lesser extent, because land is difficult to pull, and no land tide amounts to more than a few inches). This is all very well, but why should there also be a high tide at B, on the opposite side of the Earth?

It is rather misleading to say, as many books do, that the solid Earth is being 'pulled away' from the water, so let us now assume that the Moon's attraction is

59

pulling the whole of the Earth toward it. Point A, which is closest to the Moon, will be the most strongly attracted, so that the water will heap up to produce a high tide. At Point B, the reverse is true. The pull is at its weakest, so that the water tends to be 'left behind', and the result is a second high tide.

Next, assume that the Earth and the Moon are keeping at a constant distance from each other, but that the Earth is spinning round once in 24 hours. Obviously, the water-heaps – that is to say, the high tides – will not spin with it; they will keep 'under' the Moon, and the heaps will seem to sweep round the Earth once in 24 hours, so that every region will have two high tides and two low tides per day.

Now we can start to bring in some of the many complications. First, the Moon is moving along in its orbit, so that the water-heaps shift as they follow the Moon around, and on average the high tide at any particular place will be 50 minutes later each day. Neither will the two high tides be equal. In the next diagram, it is clear that there is a high tide

at C; twelve hours later, point C will have moved round C′, and will have another high tide – but this will not be equal to the first, because of the tilt of the Earth's axis (AX). If the original tide is represented by CD, the second will be represented by C′D′, which is obviously less. This is known as the 'diurnal inequality' of the tides.

Neither is the Earth really surrounded by a shallow, uniform water-shell. The seas are of various shapes and depths, and local effects are all-important. Also, the waters take some time to heap up, so that maximum tide does not occur directly 'under' the Moon; there is definite lag, and the highest tide follows the Moon after an interval which depends upon local conditions. We must, too, reckon with the effect of the Moon's changing distance from the Earth, because its gravitational pull is greatest when it is near perigee.

Next we must consider the Sun, and we are faced with a situation which may seem curious. The gravitational pull of the Sun on the Earth is much more powerful than the Moon's, but the Sun is also 400 times further away, and so far as the tides are concerned what really matters is the difference of the pull between the centre of the Earth and the point directly under the Sun. The solar tides are less than half as powerful as the lunar ones, and in this particular tug-of-war the Moon wins easily. When the Sun and the Moon are pulling in the same direction (or in exactly opposite directions, which comes to the same thing) we have strong or 'spring' tides; when the Sun and the Moon are pulling at right angles to each other, we have weaker or 'neap' tides. Spring tides, incidentally, have nothing whatsoever to do with the season of spring. They occur when the Moon is new or full, while neap tides are produced when the Moon is at half-phase. (Two astronomical terms may be worth mentioning here. When the Moon is new or full, it is said to be at 'syzygy'; at half, it is a 'quadrature'.)

Just as the Earth has slowed down the Moon's rotation, so the tides produced by the Moon are slowing down the spin of the Earth – not to anything like the same extent, but by an amount which can be measured. On average, tidal forces

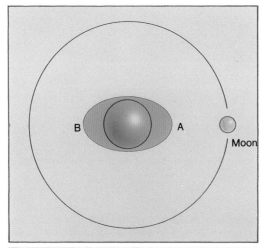

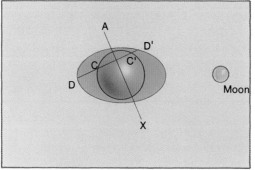

A diagram illustrating the influence of the Moon on Earth's tides. See the text for a full explanation.

Above: The Thames Barrier, completed in 1982, is designed to protect Londoners from the possibility of flooding during spring tides combined with abnormal weather conditions.

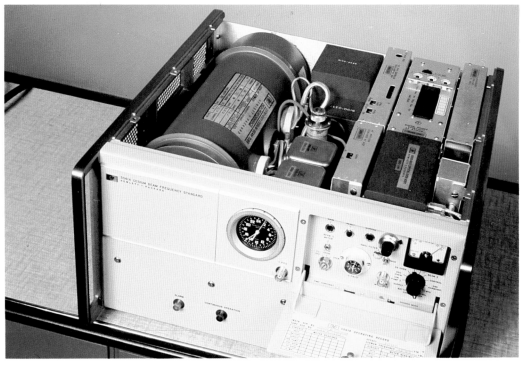

due to the Moon mean that the 'day' is becoming longer by about one-fiftieth of a second in every thousand years, which amounts to 0.00000002 of a second per day. There are complications, because there are also random variations in the speed of rotation which are due to shifts and changes taking place inside the Earth itself, and now and then we have to adjust our clocks, because modern atomic clocks are better timekeepers than the Earth (in 1990, for example, it was necessary to add a 'leap second' to make the clocks and the Earth agree).

Left: This atomic clock, from the Royal Greenwich Observatory, uses the periodic vibration of caesium atoms for the most accurate timekeeping known to date.

A solar halo around the Sun accompanied by wisps of cirrostratus cloud responsible for the effect.

reach this state, both it and Earth will be destroyed by changes in the Sun.

What about other effects which have been said to be due to the Moon? For example, it has been suggested that earthquakes may be triggered off by lunar tides produced in the Earth's mantle, but the evidence is lacking. Certainly there is no connection between the Moon and the weather. A 'ring round the Moon' does often show that rain is on the way, but the ring is produced by a high-altitude cloud of the type known as cirrostratus, at a height of rather over 6,000m (20,000ft), and it is this cloud – not the Moon itself – which gives us the warning. Plant life is similarly unaffected, and few farmers now believe, as their great-grandfathers did, that it is unwise to plant crops at the time of new moon. I will say nothing here about the astrologers, because an astrologer with genuine powers is about as common as a great auk, but I must mention the association which has been claimed to link the Moon with 'lunacy'. It is still widely believed that people with mental problems are at their very worst at the time of full moon. I find this hard to credit, but I have known some doctors who take it seriously, so I suppose that it is only fair to keep an open mind.

Finally, there is a suggestion from Jerome Pearson, in the United States, that the Earth's air would never have become breathable but for the Moon, because there would have been no magnetic field, and plants would have been unable to develop. Pearson believes that the Moon was once an independent planet, and was captured by the Earth at an early stage in the story of the Solar System. As it came inward it set up tidal friction in the interior of the Earth, producing enough heat to melt the core; the iron-rich material began to swirl around, and a magnetic field developed. Once this had happened, life could begin, so that plants spread onto the barren lands, removed much of the atmospheric carbon dioxide and replaced it with free oxygen.

All this is very speculative, and I do not pretend to be convinced about it, but it is certainly an attractive idea – so when you next look up at the Moon, I suggest that you give it a hearty vote of thanks!

Another result of the tidal interactions is that the Moon is being driven slowly away from the Earth. Its distance increases by between 3 and 4 centimetres per year (1.2–1.5in), which is not very much, but it produces effects which can be traced. As each day is 0.00000002 of a second longer than the previous day, then a century (36,525 days) ago the length of the day was shorter by 0.00073 of a second. Taking an average between then and now, the length of the day was half this value, or 0.00036 of a second, shorter than at present. But since 36,525 days have passed by, the total error is $36,525 \times 0.00036 = 13$ seconds. Therefore the position of the Moon, when calculated back, will be wrong; it will seem to have moved too far, i.e. too fast. This is the lunar 'secular acceleration'. It shows up when we calculate the times of eclipses which took place many centuries ago.

If the Moon continued to move away from the Earth at its present rate, we would finally come to a time when its distance from us was as much as 547,162 km (340,000 miles), while the 'day' and the 'month' would be equal at 47 times the length of our present day. But this cannot actually happen, because it would take too long. Well before the Moon can

Mapping the Moon

The first man to look at the Moon through a telescope was English. His name was Thomas Harriot, and at one time he was tutor to Sir Walter Raleigh. He was always interested in science, and in 1609 he managed to buy one of the newly-invented telescopes; his map of the Moon did at least show some of the main features in roughly the right positions. But it was the great Italian, Galileo, who made the first systematic use of the telescope in astronomy, and during the early part of 1610 he made a series of discoveries which led to a complete change in outlook. For example, he saw the satellites of Jupiter, the phases of Venus, the polar caps of Mars, the millions of stars in the Milky Way, and the mountains and craters of the Moon.

Anyone can see the broad, dark patches on the Moon's face. They were once thought to be seas, and are still called by romantic names such as the Sea of Tranquillity (Latin, Mare Tranquilitatis), the Ocean of Storms (Oceanus Procellarum), the Bay of Rainbows (Sinus Iridum) and so on, though for a long time now we have known that there has never been any water on the Moon, so that the 'seas' are nothing more than dry lava-beds. On the other hand there are plenty of mountains, valleys, hills, ridges and circular structures which are always called craters, though in many cases 'walled plains' would be a better term.

In 1645 a much better map of the Moon was drawn by Johann Hevelius, a wealthy amateur who lived at Danzig in Poland (the modern Gdańsk). Hevelius named the mountains after ranges on Earth, such as the Apennines and the Alps, and he also named the craters; for example, one large formation with a dark floor was christened 'the Greater Black Lake'. Hevelius' names for the craters did not last. Six years later an Italian Jesuit astronomer, Riccioli, produced a new map and had the bright idea of calling the craters after famous persons – usually, though not always, astronomers.

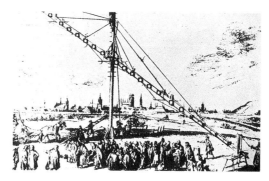

Left: The aerial telescope used by Hevelius in the 17th century. His lunar map was the best of its time.

Riccioli's system is still used, although it has been altered in some ways and many new names have been added. Some unexpected people seem to have found

Below: Giovanni Battista Riccioli's map of the Moon produced in 1651. His was the idea of calling craters after famous people.

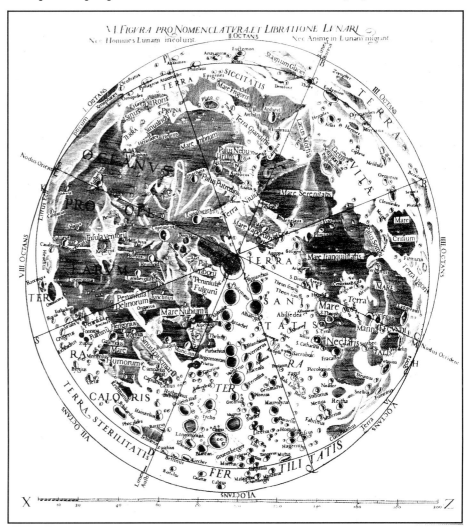

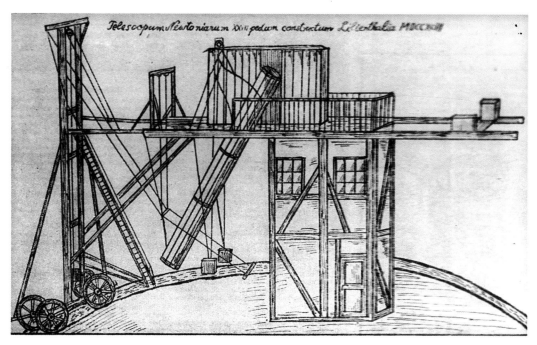

their way to the Moon. Famous astronomers such as Ptolemy, Galileo and Copernicus are there, and Riccioli was careful to name a large and important formation after himself, but we also find Julius Cæsar, not because of his conquest of Gaul but because he was responsible for a major revision of the calendar. (There is even a crater named Hell. This does not mean that it is particularly deep; it honours a Hungarian astronomer whose name really was Maximilian Hell.)

Obviously only part of the Moon could be mapped, because, as we have seen, there is a large area which is always turned away from us. Moreover, the 'libration regions' near the Moon's edge are so foreshortened that they are difficult to examine, and it is not easy to tell the difference between a crater and a mountain ridge. Although the regular craters are circular, they are drawn out into ellipses when they lie well away from the centre of the Moon's disk; for instance Plato – Riccioli's new name for the 'Greater Black Lake' – is perfectly circular, with a diameter of 96km (60 miles), but as seen from Earth appears to be oval.

The first really great observer of the Moon was Johann Hieronymus Schröter, whose lunar work began in 1778 and was brought to a sad end in 1814, when invading French troops sacked his observatory at Lilienthal, outside Bremen, and even plundered his telescopes, whose brass tubes were mistaken for gold. Schröter made excellent drawings of the lunar surface, and even estimated the heights of the mountains by measuring their shadows, but he made one bad mistake: he believed that the Moon had a reasonably dense atmosphere, and that changes were taking place on the surface all the time. Yet he did not go so far as William Herschel, who was quite convinced that the Moon was inhabited.

Herschel was Hanoverian by birth, but came to England when still a young man, and became an organist in the city of Bath (the house in which he lived for some time, No. 19 New King Street, has now been turned into a Herschel museum). During the 1770s he became interested in astronomy, and began to make his own telescopes. Then, in 1781, he was mapping the sky when he came across an object which was certainly not a star, and which proved to be a new planet, the world we now call Uranus. At once he became famous; he was made Court Astronomer to King George III, and was able to give up music as a profession, devoting all the rest of his life to astronomy. He was probably the greatest observer who has ever lived, and he was the first to give a reasonably good picture of the shape of our star-system or Galaxy, but his views about 'other life' were strangely extreme. He wrote that the habitability of the Moon was 'an absolute certainty', and he even thought that there might be intelligent beings living in a cool, pleasant region below the surface of the Sun.

There was also Franz von Paula Gruithuisen, an energetic German astronomer. In 1822, the year that Herschel died, Gruithuisen announced that he had discovered a genuine city on the Moon, with 'dark gigantic ramparts extending about 23 miles either way, and arranged on either side of a principal rampart down the centre . . . a work of art'. Actually, his 'dark gigantic ramparts' turn out to be low, haphazard ridges. (Gruithuisen was quite sincere, but he did allow his imagination to run away with him. Another of his theories was that the faint luminosity of the night side of the planet Venus was due to powerful illuminations set up by the 'Venusians' to celebrate the crowning of a new king!)

In 1833 Sir John Herschel, son of the discoverer of Uranus, took a large telescope to the Cape of Good Hope in order to study the southern stars, which can never be seen from Europe because they do not rise above the horizon. Communications were slow in those days, and a reporter on a New York paper, the *Sun*, realized that it would take Herschel some time to hear about any story which he cared to print. So the *Sun* published a series of articles in which it was claimed that Herschel had developed an entirely new type of telescope capable of showing all sorts of wonders on the Moon, ranging from sapphire rocks and active volcanoes to large white birds, blue animals with beards, and even 'a strange amphibious creature which rolled with great velocity across the pebbly beach'. The climax came with a description of lunar bat-men with yellow faces and copper-coloured hair. Many people were taken in, and it is said that a women's club in Massachusetts went so far as to write to Herschel asking him the best way to get in touch with the bat-men and convert them to Christianity. The hoax was soon exposed, but it was great fun while it lasted, and from all accounts Herschel was amused rather than annoyed.

Meanwhile two Germans, Wilhelm Beer and Johann von Mädler, had been using the small telescope at Beer's observatory to draw up a new map of the Moon. It finally appeared in 1838, and was a masterpiece of careful, accurate observation, so that it remained the best map for many years. Unlike Schröter, Beer and Mädler believed the Moon to be an airless, waterless, changeless world. The result was that many astronomers stopped looking at it; if nothing ever happened there, what was the point?

This state of affairs lasted until 1866, when Julius Schmidt, Director of the Athens Observatory, made a startling announcement. He claimed that a small, deep crater on the Sea of Serenity (Mare Serenitatis) had disappeared, to be replaced by a white patch. Actually, it now seems definite that there had been no real change, but the whole affair caused a great deal of interest, and once again

An oblique view of the far side of the Moon taken at 155 degrees E, 10 degrees S, the area west of Kepler, by Apollo 10.

many astronomers began to turn their attention back toward the Moon. New maps were drawn, and by now photography had come upon the scene.

The first lunar photograph was taken by J.W. Draper as early as 1840, and François Arago, of Paris, wrote that by using photography it would become possible to map the whole of the Moon 'in a few minutes'. Things did not turn out to be nearly so easy as that, and the first really detailed lunar atlas did not appear until 1899, but it was obviously better to use the camera instead of the human eye.

Even in our own century it was still thought possible that the Moon might have an atmosphere of some kind – much thinner than ours, but dense enough to burn up meteors, in which case there would have been shooting-stars in the lunar sky. The American astronomer W.H. Pickering studied dark patches inside some of the lunar craters and suggested that they might be due to low-type plants or even swarms of insects, while it was also thought possible that there might be deposits of frost or snow. All these ideas were swept away in the 1950s, with the beginning of the Space Age.

The first successes came in 1959, when the Russians sent three unmanned space-craft toward the Moon. In January, Luna 1 flew past at a distance of less than 6,500 km (4,000 miles), and sent back important information; for instance, it was found that the Moon has no detectable magnetic field. In the following September Luna 2 crash-landed on the surface, and then, in October, Luna 3 made a 'round trip', taking pictures of the far side and transmitting them back Earth. For the first time we were able to study the hidden part of the Moon.

Not surprisingly, the far side turned out to be very much the same as the side which we have always known. There were differences in detail, and there were fewer of the dark 'seas', but there were mountains, valleys, craters and hills. The Russians were quick to give names to the newly-found features; one huge crater, with a dark floor and a central peak, was named in honour of the great rocket pioneer Tsiolskovskii. Another feature looked as if it were a mountain range, but later pictures showed that it was nothing more than a bright streak – and the 'Soviet Mountains' were hastily removed from the maps!

Between August 1966 and August 1967 the Americans launched five Orbiter space-craft, which were put into closed paths round the Moon and sent back thousands of high-quality photographs covering almost the entire surface. When Orbiter 5 came to the end of its career, and was deliberately crashed on to the lunar surface on 31 January 1968, the task of mapping the Moon was over.

Below: The crater Daedalus on the far side of the Moon.

Bottom: In the circled area, the white object casting a shadow is Surveyor 1 sitting on the lunar surface. The picture was taken by Lunar Orbiter III on 22 February 1967 and covers an area 350 × 500 feet.

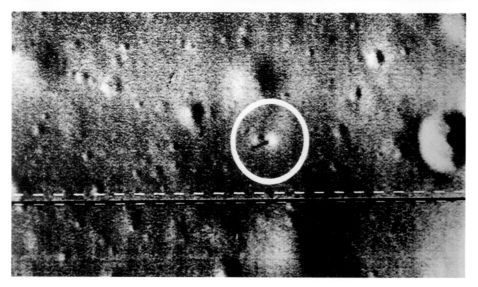

The Lunar World

To many people the Moon is much the most interesting object to observe with a small telescope, or even a pair of binoculars, because there is so much to see. Also, the aspect is always changing, because of the shifting angle of the Sun's rays. When near the terminator – that is to say, the boundary between the sunlight and dark hemispheres – a crater will be prominent, with its shadow extending across its floor; later, when the shadows shrink, it will be less easy to find, and near full moon, when the sunlight is coming straight down and there are virtually no shadows at all, a crater may be hard to identify – unless it is particularly bright, or (like Plato) has an exceptionally dark floor. Finding one's way around the Moon is not so difficult as might be thought, but it does take time and patience. Near full phase, too, the whole scene is dominated by the bright streaks or rays which come from a few of the craters, notably Tycho in the southern uplands and Copernicus in the Sea of Clouds (Mare Nubium).

In giving a brief description of the various surface features we must start with the seas, or maria, which cover large areas of the Earth-turned part of the Moon. The most prominent of them is the Mare Imbrium, or Sea of Showers, which is well-formed and is more or less circular, with mountainous borders; in the south it is bounded by the Apennines and Carpathians, while to the north are the Alps, cut through by a magnificent valley, 129km (80 miles) long, which is a fine sight when illuminated at a suitable angle. There are craters on the Mare Imbrium, but the whole area is much smoother than the brighter regions which were once called 'lands', though this term has now fallen out of favour.

As seen with the naked eye, the Mare Imbrium is to the upper left of the disk as seen by an observer in the northern hemisphere of the Earth. However, most astronomical telescopes give an upside-down or inverted image, so that Mare Imbrium is to the lower right.

Not all the seas are as regular as the Mare Imbrium, and not all have lofty, mountainous borders. For example the Oceanus Procellarum or Ocean of Storms – larger than our Mediterranean – is much less well-defined, while the Mare Frigoris or Sea of Cold is long and narrow, so that it gives the impression of being nothing more than a lava overflow. Note, too, that most of the major *maria* are connected; thus there is a break in the mountains between the Mare Imbrium and the adjacent Mare Serenitatis (Sea of Serenity), while the Mare Serenitatis is in turn joined to the Mare Tranquillitatis (Sea of Tranquillity), where the first Apollo astronauts landed in 1969. Some of the seas are fairly regular, but lead out of larger mare areas – for example, the Mare Humorum (Sea of Humours) and the Mare Nectaris (Sea of Nectar).

The Mare Crisium (Sea of Crises) is exceptional in being detached. It is clearly visible with the naked eye, and contains few well-marked craters. It seems to be elongated in a north-south direction, but actually the east-west diameter is slightly greater; we have to allow for foreshortening. There are, too, some *maria* which are so close to the limb that from Earth it is difficult to identify them at all. One of these is the Mare Orientale or Eastern Sea, between the Oceanus Procellarum and the limb. It is so badly placed that it cannot be seen except when the libration is at its most favourable. I had the honour of discovering it and naming it, when I was charting the lunar libration regions long before the Space Age – but by a decree of the International Astronomical Union, passed in 1966, 'east' and 'west' were officially reversed, so that my *Eastern* Sea is now on the Moon's western limb!

The lunar *mountains* are lofty, for example some of the peaks in the Apennines rise to more than 4,570m (15,000 ft) above the general surface. Their heights are measured by the shadows which they cast (as was first done by Galileo, and later, more accurately, by Schröter). There are many other ranges, such as the Hæmus Mountains which

This photographic map of the Moon was prepared for the Apollo 8 astronauts who were to survey sites for the first moon landing. Site 3 was ultimately chosen.

form the southern border of the Mare Serenitatis, and there are also many isolated peaks and clumps of hills. Pico, north of Plato and on the floor of the Mare Imbrium, is a splendid example of a lunar peak – and look too at the Straight Range, nearby, which really is straight, and seems very curious indeed.

Of course the whole of the Moon is dominated by the *craters*. They are everywhere; they cluster thickly in the bright uplands, but are also to be found

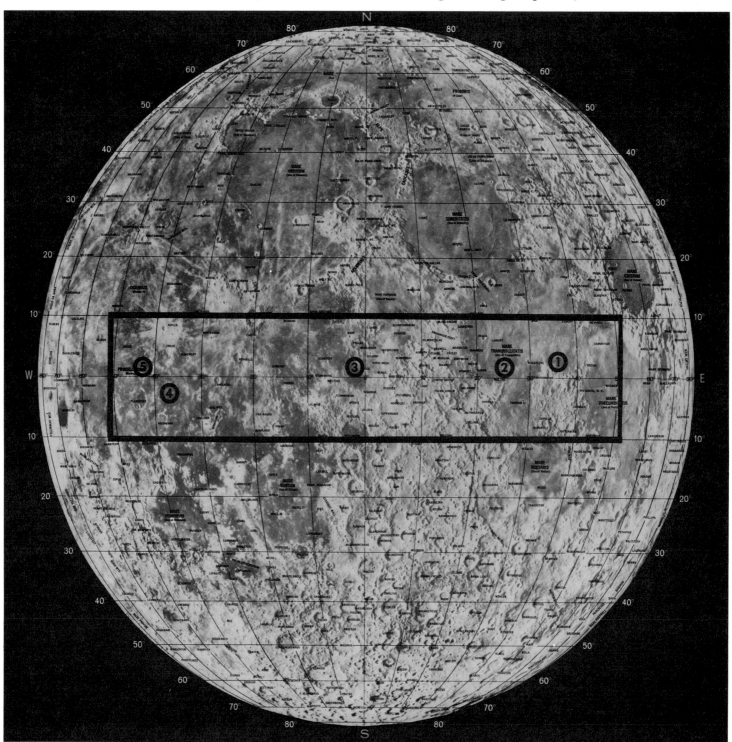

on the floors of the *maria* and even on the tops of mountains. Basically a lunar crater is circular, but may have been damaged and distorted by later formations, and there are many cases of craters which have been so battered that they have been reduced to low-walled, incomplete 'ghosts'.

It would be wrong to regard a crater as a deep, steep-sided well or mine-shaft. True, the floors may be far below the level of the outer wall – over 6,000m (20,000ft) in a few instances – but the walls themselves do not generally rise high above the outer surface, and if a crater could be seen in profile it would be rather like a shallow saucer. Neither do the central mountains ever reach the height of the ramparts. In fact, if you could put a lid over a Moon crater, it would not even graze the top of any peak inside.

Some of the craters have massive,

Left: The lunar surface. The Apennines and Alps run from top right to centre. The Mare Serenitatis is to the left.

This view of the lunar horizon was taken from the Command Service Module of Apollo 12 and shows a spectacular view of the crater Eratosthenes.

69

The first close-up photograph of the crater Copernicus, taken by Lunar Orbiter II with a telephoto lens. The picture looks due north from the crater's southern rim. Mountains rising from the flat floor of the crater are 300m (984ft) high with slopes up to 30 degrees. The 900m (2,950ft) mountain on the horizon is the Gay Lussac promontory in the Carpathian mountains.

terraced walls. This is the case, for example, with Copernicus on the Mare Nubium and Theophilus on the edge of the Mare Nectaris, both of which are around 96km (60 miles) in diameter, and both of which have central mountain groups. Others have no major central mountains, and have flattish floors, Plato being a good example. Another large formation which lacks a central peak is Ptolemeus, near the apparent centre of the disk, which has a diameter of 148km (92 miles), but whose walls are rather low.

Ptolemeus is the northernmost member of a group of three large walled plains; the other members are Alphonsus and Arzachel. There are, in fact, many examples of chains and groups of craters, so that the distribution over the lunar surface is not random. Look, for example, at the great trio of Theophilus, Cyrillus and Catharina, or at the group on the Mare Imbrium consisting of Archimedes, Arisillus and Autolycus, while on the western limb we find the huge, dark-floored Grimaldi and Ric-

cioli, together with a rather smaller crater, Hevel, which has a convex floor and a comparatively low central peak. Down the eastern limb there is a tremendous line of large enclosures, from Furnerius in the south through Petavius, Vendelinus, Langrenus, Cleomedes and Endymion; even the Mare Crisium may be regarded as belonging to this chain.

Some craters have brilliant walls. Brightest of all is Aristarchus on the Oceanus Procellarum; it is only 37km (23 miles) in diameter, but it glitters even when illuminated only by Earthshine, and no less an observer than William Herschel several times mistook it for an erupting volcano. Proclus, near the edge of the Mare Crisium, is another small, brilliant crater, and there are many others.

Though the typical crater has a sunken floor, there are a few exceptions, of which the most famous is Wargentin, near the south-west limb. It is 88.5km (55 miles) across, and has a floor which is filled to the brim with lava, so that it has taken on the appearance of a plateau.

The landing site of Apollo 15, showing a huge rill.

When one crater breaks into another, as happens thousands upon thousands of times, it is almost always the rule that the smaller crater intrudes into the larger, so that again we have an obviously non-random distribution. There are, too, many instances of chains of small craterlets which have run together. The so-called Rheita Valley, in the south-eastern uplands, is of this type; it is badly named, because it is not a true valley at all.

Rills, alternatively known as rilles or clefts, are crack-like features which may extend for many miles, and look superficially rather like cracks in dried mud. Some of them are easy to see; perhaps the best example is the Ariadeus Rill, near the Mare Vaporum (Sea of Vapours) which is well over 160km (100 miles) long. Close by it is the Hyginus Rill, which is in part a craterlet-chain; Hyginus itself is 6.4km (4 miles) across. There are whole systems of rills here and there, and there are also rills on the floors of craters. A very prominent rill can be seen inside the great walled plain Petavius, running from the central mountain out toward the south-western wall.

Near the brilliant Aristarchus and its darker companion crater Herodotus is a particularly interesting, rather U-shaped valley, often known as Schröter's Valley in honour of its discoverer. When suitably illuminated it is a truly splendid sight.

Faults are fairly common, but not many of them are prominent. The leading example is the Straight Wall, near the eastern edge of the Mare Nubium, which is not straight, and is not a wall! The level of the ground to the west drops by 250m (800ft), so that an observer standing to the east of it would be at the top of a fairly steeply-inclined drop while an observer standing to the east would be looking at a cliff. Its total length is 130km (80 miles). In the not-too-distant future, it will no doubt become a tourist attraction . . .

Domes are of interest. They are low swellings in the ground, often with summit craterlets. They are not too easy to find, because they are so low, but they are quite plentiful in some areas.

Then, of course, there are the *rays*, coming from a few special craters. Near full moon two ray systems, those from

The Oceanus Procellarum, photographed in 1966 by Commander H.R. Hatfield, R.N. The rayed crater is Kepler.

Tycho and Copernicus, are so conspicuous that they almost drown the rest of the detail, though there are other ray-centres too. Because they cover all other formations, they are clearly surface features, and when the sunlight strikes them at a low angle they cannot be seen. The Tycho and Copernicus rays do not issue from the centres of the craters themselves, but are tangential to the walls. The minor rays associated with the craterlet-pair of Messier and Messier A, in the Mare Fecunditatis (Sea of Fertility) come out in one direction only.

To my mind, the most beautiful sight on the whole of the Moon is the Sinus Iridum (Bay of Rainbows), which leads off the Mare Imbrium. When the Sun is rising there, the solar rays naturally catch the tops of the mountains first, and the mountainous border of the Bay seems to project into the darkness, causing the appearance which is often called the Jewelled Handle. It does not last for long, but when you see it you cannot mistake it.

The question of how the craters were formed has caused endless arguments, which are not over even yet. All sorts of weird theories have been put forward (coral atolls, for example), but my favourite is the idea due to a Spanish engineer, Sixto Ocampo, who claimed in 1949 that the craters were bomb-pits, produced during a nuclear war. The fact that some craters have central mountains while others do not proves, of course, that the two opposing sides used different kinds of bombs!

Most modern astronomers believe that the craters and *maria* are impact structures. After its formation, around 4,600 million years ago, the Moon suffered a prolonged bombardment by meteorites; this continued from about 4,200 million to 3,900 million years ago, so that the main 'seas' such as the Mare Imbrium were formed at this time as well as many craters. Then, between 3,900 million and 3,100 million years ago, there was tremendous volcanic activity; magma welled out from inside the Moon and flooded the basins, producing the *maria* which we see today. After that the Moon became more or less inert, apart from the occasional production of new impact craters. On this picture even the youngest of the major craters, such as Tycho, are very ancient by terrestrial standards, and date back well into our pre-Cambrian.

The agreement is not universal, and it

A view of a large boulder field in the Taurus-Littrow mountains southwest of the Serenitatis Basin. The picture was taken by Apollo 17.

has also been claimed that the main craters and *maria* are of internal origin, so that they are more nearly related to volcanic calderas than to impact structures such as the Meteorite Crater in Arizona. The non-random distribution of the craters does not indicate a haphazard bombardment, for example. This is no place to go into detail; my own view is that the main crater-forming process has been internal, but I recognize that at the present moment this is very much of a minority view.

In any case, there is little activity on the Moon now. There are reliable reports of local glows and obscurations, and these seem to be due to minor gaseous outbreaks from below the crust, but there is certainly nothing violent enough to cause an obvious change in the surface features.

Before the Space Age there was a great deal about the Moon which we did not know, quite apart from the fact that over 40 per cent of the surface was permanently hidden from us. There was even a strange theory that the lunar seas were filled with soft dust, in which case manned landings there would have been out of the question. But all this was changed during the 1960s; the Moon was at last within our reach.

It was once thought that the surface of the Moon, particularly the Mare, would be covered by thick, soft dust. This proved not to be the case, but nevertheless a substantial amount of dust is to be found, as can be seen at the base of this boulder (Apollo 17).

Missions
to the Moon

'Men might as well try to reach the Moon as to cross the stormy North Atlantic by means of steam power.' Such were the words of an eminent scientist, Dr. Dionysius Lardner, addressing the British Association in 1840. The Atlantic was soon conquered, but the first flight to the Moon had to wait for a little longer – in fact until 20 July 1969, when Neil Armstrong and Edwin Aldrin, in the lunar module of Apollo 11, came down in the barren Sea of Tranquillity. At that moment I was in a BBC television studio, carrying out a live commentary; I had returned from a conference in America a day or two earlier. When I heard Neil Armstrong's voice: 'The *Eagle* has landed', I was only one of millions of

Astronaut Edwin Aldrin Jr, lunar module pilot for Apollo 11, prepares to deploy the Early Apollo Scientific Experiments Package (EASEP). The picture was taken by Neil Armstrong.

people all round the world who felt a surge of relief. Hours later Neil Armstrong stepped out on to the Moon, and we heard the words which will never be forgotten: 'That's one small step for a man – one giant leap for mankind.'

It was indeed a giant leap, and the mission was dangerous by any standards, if only because even then the true nature of the Moon's surface was uncertain. The 'dust drift' theory had been disproved, because American and Russian unmanned vehicles had made controlled landings without showing any sign of sinking out of sight, but there was one major weakness in the whole Apollo

planning: there was no provision for rescue. Had the lunar module not made a perfect touch-down, it could not have taken off again. Moreover, there was only one ascent engine, and this had to work faultlessly at the first attempt.

All went well, and Armstrong and Aldrin were able to make a two-hour foray on to the lunar surface, which Aldrin described so aptly as 'magnificent desolation'. There was no problem in walking around under the low lunar gravity, and the whole moonwalk was seen by television viewers all over the world, who were able to watch as the two astronauts moved around, seemingly in

Landing sites for the Apollo series. At the time the map was prepared, only Apollo 11 and 12 had completed their missions, Apollo 11 in July 1969 and Apollo 12 in November of the same year.

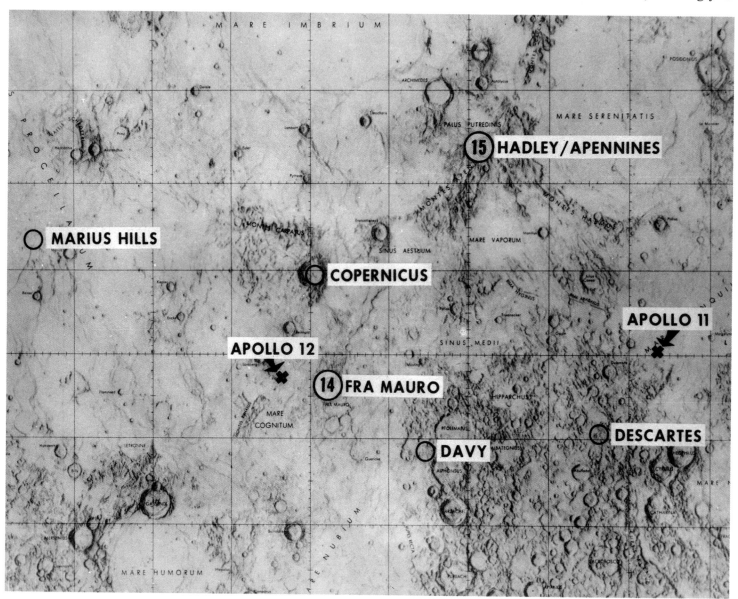

76

'slow motion'. Samples were collected, and scientific experiments were set up before Armstrong and Aldrin went back inside the module, later to blast back to rendezvous with Michael Collins, who had remained orbiting the Moon in the main part of Apollo 11.

In November 1969 came Apollo 12, taking astronauts Conrad and Bean to the Moon. This time the landing site was in the Oceanus Procellarum, close to the old Surveyor 3 automatic probe which had been on the Moon ever since April 1967; Conrad and Bean were able to walk over to it and break parts of it off to bring home for analysis. But Apollo 13, launched in April 1970, was a near-disaster. On the outward journey there was a violent explosion, and it was only by a combination of courage, skill and (frankly) luck that astronauts Lovell, Haise and Swigert survived unharmed.

This was the low point of the whole programme. Four more missions followed, all of them successful. Apollo 14 (February 1971) was commanded by Alan Shepard, who had been the first American in space a mere ten years earlier; he and Thomas Mitchell landed near the ruined crater Fra Mauro, in the Mare Nubium, and took a 'cart' to carry their equipment, so that they were able to cover a distance of over two miles. With the last three missions there was a new development. Lunar Roving Vehicles or 'moon cars' were taken along, so that the astronauts could drive around the surface. Apollo 15, with David Scott and James Irwin, landed in the foothills of the Apennines, and drove to the very edge of a great valley. Apollo 16, carrying John Young and Charles Duke, made the first landing in the highlands, in the region of the crater Descartes; and finally Apollo 17, with Eugene Cernan and Harrison Schmitt, came down in the region of the clumps of hills known as the Taurus Mountains, not far from the edge of the Mare Serenitatis. Dr. Schmitt was a geologist who had been given astronaut

Lunar Module Pilot (Apollo 15) James Irwin pictured next to the Lunar Roving Vehicle with Mount Hadley in the background.

The first automated rover to travel across the lunar surface was Lunokhod 1, carried there by Luna 17. The central 'tub' of the vehicle was pressurized and its control electronics were kept at a pressure of 1 Earth atmosphere. Lunokhod 1 operated for just under a year.

training specially for the mission, and as yet he remains the only professional scientist who has been to the Moon.

Meanwhile, the Russians were not idle. Their vehicle Luna 9 had made the first controlled landing, in January 1966, in the Oceanus Procellarum, so that the dust-drift theory was finally abandoned. In 1970 Luna 16 landed in the Mare Fecunditatis, grabbed a hundred grams of material and brought it back for analysis, and later there were two more sample-and-return probes, Lunas 20 (1972) and 24 (1976), both of which obtained material from the Mare Crisium area. Equally notable were the two Lunokhods, of 1970 and 1973, which were wheeled vehicles; they were taken to the Moon by Lunas and then made to move around the surface, so that they could take photographs and carry out experiments of various kinds. Lunokhod 1 travelled over six miles in the Mare Imbrium and sent back 20,000 pictures during its 11 months of operation, and Lunokhod 2, which was landed near the incomplete crater Le Monnier, not too far from the region which had been explored from Apollo 17, was almost as prolific. Though they have long since ceased to function, we know exactly where they are, and in the future they will no doubt be collected and taken away to a lunar museum. This will also be the case with the Moon-cars left by the last three Apollos. Since there is no 'weather' on the airless Moon, there is nothing to damage them, and all that need be done is to fit them with new batteries and simply drive them off.

The only lunar mission since that time has been Hagomoro 1, which was the first Japanese effort. It was launched in January 1990, and entered a closed path round the Moon in the following March. So let us now see just what the various expeditions have told us.

The outermost layer of the Moon is rather loose, and is termed the regolith; although there are no deep drifts there is plenty of dust, and this can be irritating because, as Commander Cernan told me, 'it gets into everything'. The regolith is rather variable in depth – around one metre in the maria and about twice this in the highlands; in the Taurus area visited by Apollo 17 it seemed to go down to over 15.2m (50ft) in places, but in some parts of the Descartes region, surveyed by Apollo 16, there was only a very thin layer. It is generally thought to have been produced by the pulverizing action of meteoritic particles hitting the Moon. There has been plenty of time for this to happen, and there is definite evidence of 'churning', so that external action must have been responsible.

Like the Earth, the Moon has been found to have a crust, a mantle and a core. Both crust and mantle are thicker than ours, probably because the temperatures deep inside the Moon are much lower. The crustal thickness is between 48 and 64km (30–40 miles), though it may be more in places; below it comes the mantle, which goes down to 960km (600 miles) or so, and below this again is the so-called asthenosphere, which is probably a region of partial melting. The core may be between 480 and 640km (300–400 miles) across, and is presumably rich in iron. The temperature seems to be of the order of 3000 degrees Fahrenheit, which is quite appreciable; the old idea of a Moon which is cold throughout its globe has been shown to be wrong.

If there is an iron-rich core we might expect a magnetic field, but so far we have not found one. On the other hand there seem to be 'localized' areas where there is magnetized material, and it may well be that in its past history the Moon used to have a magnetic field which has now disappeared. Orbiting vehicles have located several magnetized regions, particularly on the far side of the Moon in the region of the crater which has been named Van de Graaff.

Orbiters have also tracked down regions where the density of the sub-surface is greater than average. When passing over an unusually dense region, a

The outermost layer of the Moon is called the regolith and is quite loose, as can be seen from the footprints of the Apollo astronauts.

lunar satellite will be first speeded up and then pulled back, so that its speed will vary; in this way we have identified mascons – a word derived from *mass concentrations* – below some of the regular *maria* as well as below some of the large walled plains. They are certainly not due to buried meteorites, as was first suggested, and are more probably regions of dense volcanic rock.

Our knowledge of the Moon's interior depends mainly upon the seismometers or 'moonquake recorders' which were set up by the Apollo astronauts. They work in the same way as ordinary seismometers, but can be made more sensitive, because the Moon is so inert by our standards – for instance there are no passing lorries, or sea-waves beating against the shore! Moonquakes are common, some of them shallow and others very deep-seated, but they are very mild by our standards, and will be of no danger to future lunar bases.

As expected, no new materials were found on the Moon, and the rocks are essentially the same as ours and are of around the same age, though they are in some cases differently made up because they solidified under very different conditions. There were some extremely interesting moments, particularly during the Apollo 17 mission, when Dr. Schmitt discovered what was at first called 'orange soil' and was believed to be due to recent volcanic activity – but which, rather to everyone's disappointment, turned out to be due to small, coloured glassy particles well over three and a half thousand million years old. There was absolutely no trace of life, either past or present, and neither were there any materials which had contained water in any form, so that the old science-fiction idea of breaking up the Moon's rocks and extracting moisture has had to be cast aside. The first Apollo astronauts were strictly quarantined after their return to make sure that they had brought back nothing harmful but quarantining was abandoned after Apollo 14 because it had become so obvious that the Moon is, and always has been, totally sterile.

With the blast-off from the Moon of Eugene Cernan and Harrison Schmitt, in December 1972, the first phase of lunar exploration came to an end, but now, less than 20 years later, there is serious talk of a return there. Indeed, it seems that this must happen before long. I well remember what Eugene Cernan said to me not so many months ago: 'We'll go back. There will be others who will follow in our footsteps.'

The structure of the Moon. The loose upper layer, or regolith, while shallow over the seas, can be as deep as 20m (65ft). Below this is more solid rock down to about 25km (15 miles) succeeded by a layer of feldspar-rich rock 35km (21 miles) deep. The material is then dense again for some 800km (500 miles). The core is 1,000–1,200km (620–745 miles) thick.

The Apollo 11 crewmen, wearing biological isolation garments, arrive aboard the USS *Hornet* during recovery operations in the Pacific.

The Lunar Base

It has often been claimed that there is no point in spending money upon space research when there is so much to be done at home. This is quite a common attitude, even today, but it is not a very intelligent one, because no branch of science can now be separated from any other branch; astronomy and space research are linked with physics, chemistry, biology and medical research just as closely as arithmetic is linked with algebra. Neither is it true that the sums of money spent upon space are high by national standards. No probe to the Moon can cost as much as a couple of nuclear submarines.

Then, too, there is the international aspect. Space is of importance to us all, wherever we live, and there are encouraging signs that the great nations are starting to work together. If we cannot manage to do so, we will never get very far – and we will not deserve to do so.

Space-stations already exist (the Russian Mir was the first) and within a few years there will be more, so that a base on the Moon is the next step. Up to now we have made only reconnaissance trips; Apollo could do no more than send two astronauts to the Moon, leave them there for a brief period and then bring them back. Yet the Apollo missions were vital, because they showed, once and for all, that the Moon is a place to which men can go. We have established that landing on the surface is safe, and we have also been able to analyze Moon rocks – something which had been out of the question before the Space Age; it has been suggested that some special types of meteorites come from the Moon, but the evidence is far from clear.

The present-day mood was summed up on 20 July 1989 by President George Bush. It was the 20th anniversary of the Apollo 11 landing, and Mr. Bush committed the United States to the setting-up of a Lunar Base, though unlike President Kennedy's commitment to a lunar landing in the early 1960s he did not lay down a definite time-scale (certainly it would have been foolish to

America's only experience of long duration spaceflight was the Skylab programme in the early 1970s. The missions were successful despite the station being damaged on launch. This photograph is of Skylab 3 mission, which ran from July to September 1973.

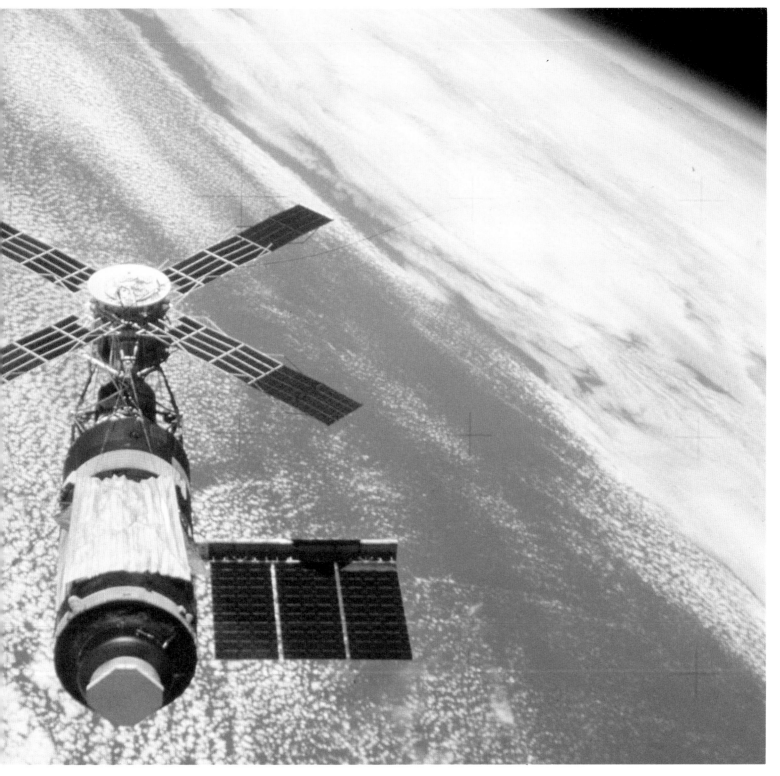

The European Space Agency's X-ray observatory EXOSAT was operational from May 1983 to April 1986 and in that time made 1,780 detailed observations of a wide variety of objects including active galactic nuclei, stellar cornoae, white dwarfs and supernovae remnants.

do so!). But let us now see what uses could be made of a station on the Moon.

First, of course, it is obvious that the Moon is an ideal site for an astronomical observatory. There are two main reasons: the lack of atmosphere, and the weak gravity. Apollo confirmed that the Moon's atmosphere is absolutely negligible, and its whole mass is no more than that of the air contained inside the Royal Festival Hall. On Earth, the air is a real problem to the astronomer; it is dirty and unsteady, and it also blocks out many of the incoming radiations, so that we are rather in the position of a pianist who is trying to play a concerto on a piano which lacks everything but its middle octave. To give just one example, consider X-rays, which are sent out by many bodies in space. They cannot penetrate the layers in the upper air, and to study them we must 'go up', which means using

rockets; X-ray astronomy could not begin before rockets became sufficiently powerful, which was not until 1963. The same is true of most other regions of the whole range of wavelengths, which we call the 'electromagnetic spectrum'. From the Earth's surface we can study only visible light, plus a certain amount of infra-red and a part of the radio range. Everything else is screened out.

Moreover, light passing through the atmosphere is bound to be 'shaken around', which is why stars twinkle. It will never be possible to make optical telescopes of really immense size. There are no such limitations on the Moon, and even construction will be much easier, because everything 'weighs' so much less; remember, the Moon's surface gravity is only one-sixth of ours. In theory, there is no reason why we should not build a reflecting telescope with a mirror

84

at least 15m (50ft) in diameter, and a tentative plan has already been made.

Compare this with the largest single-mirror telescope ever made on Earth – the Russian 236-inch, which, to be honest, has never been a success – or the one major telescope which has so far been launched into orbit round the Earth, the HST or Hubble Space Telescope, whose mirror is a mere 238cm (94ins) across. Our proposed lunar telescope would be able to 'see' objects forty times fainter than the HST can do; turn it toward Earth, look at a ten-pence coin, and you would be able to see the Queen's head.

According to the present plan, the main mirror of the lunar telescope will be made up of segments, fitted together to produce the correct curve. This has already been done on Earth, but it will be much easier on the Moon.

Large telescopes can be 'linked together', so that their light-grasp is combined. An array of giant telescopes on the surface of the Moon would be capable of looking into the extreme depths of the universe, and studying systems which are well beyond our present range of around 14,000 million light-years. We could possibly decide whether

The primary mirror of the Hubble Space Telescope is 2.4m (8ft) in diameter and weighs 820kg (1,800lb). Following its launch in May 1990, the mirror was found to suffer from spherical aberration and did not have the resolving power that had been predicted.

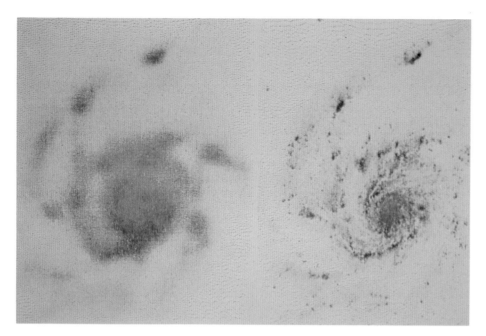

Above: This computer-enhanced photograph shows (on the left) a spiral galaxy as it appears from an optical telescope on Earth and (on the right) as it will appear through the Hubble Space Telescope.

and there would be no shortage of suitable constructional materials on the Moon. Another advantage would be the slow lunar rotation. Once an object rose in the sky, it would not set again for a period equal to almost two Earth weeks, and this would be a great help to the engineers.

There would be no problem with ground movements. From this point of view the Moon is a hundred million times more inert than the Earth. Not even the most powerful moonquake would cause a tremor of more than a millionth of an inch, and probably much less.

Stray light has become a menace on the Earth; during the 1980s, for example, the 100-inch reflector at Mount Wilson in California, for many years much the most powerful in the world, was temporarily 'mothballed' because the lights from Los Angeles had made the sky too bright for delicate astronomical observations. There is also concern at Palomar, with its 200-inch reflector, because of the lights of the city of San Diego. Even in really remote places – such as the top of Mauna Kea, or the Atacama Desert in Chile, site of three of the world's major observatories – the sky is never entirely dark. This is partly

or not the 'observable universe' is of limited extent. Stars would show up as disks rather than dots of light, and we would be able to see surface details on them; we might even detect planets associated with them – something which is likely to be beyond the powers of the HST.

The mounting of the lunar telescope could be lightweight by our standards,

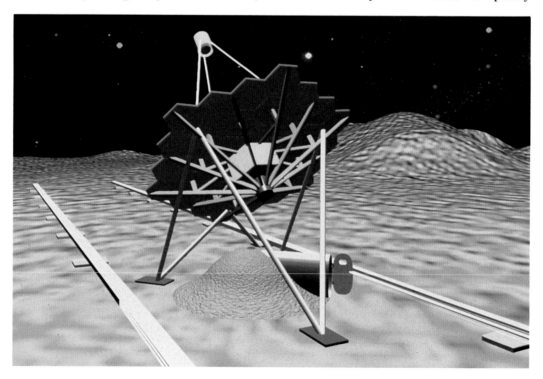

Right: Computer graphic of a possible design for a lunar telescope.

because of natural airglow, about which we can do nothing, but also because of artificial illuminations. There is no such problem on the Moon. There will be one special advantage for radio astronomers.

Long-wavelength radiations from space are collected by special instruments which are really in the form of large aerials, but which are known, rather misleadingly, as radio telescopes. Some of them are 'dishes', of which the most famous is the 250-foot instrument at Jodrell Bank in Cheshire, known as the Lovell Telescope in honour of Professor Sir Bernard Lovell, who master-minded it in the 1950s. A radio telescope does not produce a visible image (you certainly cannot look through it!) and the usual end product is a trace on a graph, but it can provide us with information which we could never obtain in any other way. Light pollution is not a problem, but radio interference is, and is becoming worse and worse with the development of commercial and military radio installations. Sir Bernard Lovell has gone so far as to say that unless something is done, radio astronomy from the Earth's surface will be a science limited entirely to the second half of the twentieth century.

The Moon is clearly a better site – particularly the far side, always turned away from the Earth, which is completely radio quiet. Moreover, we need very large dishes, and under the low lunar gravity this could be managed; it is not outrageous to think about radio telescopes several miles across. A gigantic dish, perhaps built inside a lunar crater, would have power beyond anything we could achieve either on the Earth or on a space-station. It would, of course, be absolutely stable, and it too could be linked with other dishes. One possibility is to link a lunar radio telescope with a similar instrument on Earth, giving us a baseline of a quarter of a million miles.

There have already been searches for artificial signals from space. (The first attempt was made thirty years ago by radio astronomers at Green Bank in Virginia; the experiment was known officially as Project Ozma, after the famous Wizard of Oz, but more generally as Project Little Green Men. The results were negative.) It is hard to believe that

life on Earth is unique; if we visualize an earthlike planet moving round a sunlike star, why should there not be life of the same sort as ours? And if these 'other men' have developed along similar lines, and have not blown themselves to pieces with atomic bombs (as we are at present in danger of doing), they could have developed radio telescopes. True, we are still limited by the fact that radio waves

Jodrell Bank radio telescope, near Manchester, England, now known as the Lovell Telescope.

On 26 January 1983, the Infra-Red Astronomical Satellite (IRAS) was launched to perform the first all-sky survey at infrared wavelengths. 95 percent of the sky was mapped before the telescope's liquid helium coolant ran out in November 1983.

move at 'only' 186,000 miles per second, and must take years to move from the Earth even to the nearest star, but the possibilities for communication exist.

Some instruments, such as those used for collecting infra-red radiations from space, have to be cooled down to very low temperatures of only a degree or two above absolute zero – minus 472 degrees Fahrenheit ($-273°$C), which is the coldest temperature possible. On Earth, or in space, this has to be done by using liquid helium, which is difficult to handle and is bound to evaporate, so that no infra-red telescope in space can last for very long before it becomes too 'hot'. On

the Moon there are some craters, near the lunar poles, whose floors receive no sunlight at all, because they are permanently in shadow. This means that they are almost unbelievably cold, and an infra-red telescope set up there would not have to be cooled down any further.

All this may sound attractive, but of course there are difficulties too, quite apart from the question of transport. The Moon's lack of air means that there is no protection from small meteoritic particles which must bombard the surface all the time. Our air burns away shooting-star meteors, and also brakes the even smaller particles (micrometeorites) which are too small to cause luminous effects; on the Moon there may have to be some way of protecting telescope mirrors from impacts. Neither is there any shield against harmful radiations, and we must also reckon with cosmic-ray particles; the Moon has no protective magnetic field. Also, there is a tremendous difference between the day and night temperatures, and there will be thermal strains on equipment, unless it is set up in one of the permanently shadowed areas.

Astronomy will not be the only science to benefit from a Lunar Base: far from it. As a physical and chemical laboratory site the Moon will be unrivalled, and there will also be the possibility of medical research which could even lead on to controlling diseases such as cancer, which claim so many human lives every year. And the Base will cost only a tiny fraction of the amount of money spent by the great nations during the war from 1939 to 1945!

There will have to be a steady stream of vehicles between the Earth and the Moon, which presumably means using rockets. It has been suggested that non-

Left: Two views of the Andromeda Galaxy, the upper one taken through an optical telescope, the lower with the Infra-Red Astronomical Telescope (IRAS).

fragile goods might be fired away from the Moon by means of space-guns, and this does not seem to be out of the question; it would be ironical if the

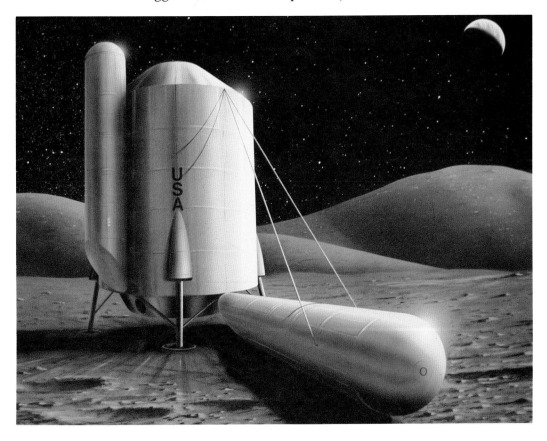

Left: Artist's impression of a possible structure for a lunar base. It is likely that the emphasis for the early 21st century will be on space stations rather than lunar bases.

An early NASA concept for a lunar base.

famous novel by Jules Verne, in which the 'astronauts' were fired moonward from the barrel of a huge cannon, turned out to have an element of truth in it – though certainly it could never be used for human travel, and neither could it be used from the Earth's surface, because the projectile would be burned away by friction even before it left the mouth of the cannon.

Commercial mining of lunar materials seems rather unlikely, both because of the problems of getting material home and because it does not seem as if there is anything valuable enough to mine. Neither can we have any hope of turning the Moon into a sort of second Earth. We cannot give it an atmosphere, and even if we could do so the Moon would be unable to hold it down. Once there, we must remain permanently inside our space-craft, inside our space-suits, or inside our pressurized base. What the Lunar Base will be like remains to be seen. Early pioneers, such as Wernher

von Braun, pictured graceful domes kept up by the pressure of atmosphere inside them, and fitted with airlocks, so that the colonists could normally wear ordinary clothing; this may well turn out to be close to the mark, but we must agree that the numbers of people living on the Moon will always be limited. There is no chance of solving our over-population problem in that way.

What about our next steps? Mars must be first on the list, and it is quite likely that journeys there will start from the Moon rather than directly from the Earth, but again we must wait and see.

There is already talk of 'holidays on the Moon'. These may come eventually, if not yet awhile; in the coming centuries I would not be at all surprised to see advertisements for tours to the Straight Wall or the Alpine Valley. At least it is quite likely that we will see a Lunar Base in the foreseeable future, so that there will be two inhabited worlds in the Solar System instead of only one.

The Earth in the Future

We have looked at the past history of the Earth and its Moon; now let us see whether we can look into the future, and decide what is in store for us.

From the cosmical point of view, nothing much is likely to happen for a very long time. Slight changes in the Earth's path and the tilt of its axis, and perhaps minor variations in the solar output, may produce another Ice Age, but it is not likely to be more severe than the cold period which ended 10,000 years ago. There is always the danger of a major impact from a wandering asteroid, but even if this happened we would no doubt be able to cope with it better than the dinosaurs did (even assuming that the dinosaurs were indeed destroyed by a collision some 65 million years ago, which is very far from certain). Of course, it is always possible that a third world war would render the whole world permanently uninhabitable, but that would be our own fault, while if we are damaging the ozone layer by our chemicals, or causing a greenhouse effect by releasing too much carbon dioxide into the air, we have enough leeway to put matters right. In the long run, the real danger will come from the Sun itself.

When it first settled down to its period of stable existence, around five thousand million years ago, the Sun was not so luminous as it is now. Gradually it heated up, and the temperatures in the inner part of the Solar System rose, with varied effects upon the planets. Mercury was never massive enough to hold down much in the way of atmosphere, but Venus and the Earth may well have started to evolve along similar lines, with oceans, atmospheres and even primitive life. When the Sun's power increased, the Earth was sufficiently far out to escape the worst effects, but Venus, more than twenty million miles closer in, was not – so that its oceans evaporated, the carbonates were driven out of the rocks,

and there was what may be termed a runaway greenhouse effect, so that in a relatively short time Venus turned into the furnace-like world of today, with any life there relentlessly wiped out. It is sobering to reflect that if the Earth had been only slightly closer to the Sun, the same thing might have happened here.

But our world was safe, and will be safe as long as the Sun remains in its present condition. Unfortunately there must come a time when the supply of hydrogen 'fuel' will run low, and then the Sun must change its whole structure.

The first sign of alarm will be a marked increase in luminosity as different sorts of reactions begin, so that the Sun's core shrinks and heats up. In several thousand million years from now the Earth's climate will have changed, with Hudson's Bay and North Norway becoming as warm as the present Mexico, with the equator so hot that life there will be very difficult indeed. The heating will go on

The Helix Nebula. This faint object is the nearest planetary nebula to Earth at 400 light years. The outer red shell is due to ionised hydrogen and nitrogen and is matter thrown off by the central star. This will probably be the fate of our Sun in some far distant future.

The Planetary Nebula NGC 6302. The explosion of the central star in this nebula was particularly violent and the gases ejected are travelling at some 400km/sec.

until the surface temperature of the Earth has risen by a hundred degrees, so that the oceans will evaporate. Just when this will happen we cannot be sure; it may be in no more than four thousand million years, or it may be considerably longer, but sooner or later the Sun will become a red giant star, and there is no chance that life on Earth can survive.

This will not be all. When the Sun reaches its peak luminosity its diameter will be a hundred times greater than it is now – that is to say, at least 80 million miles, so that it will swallow up Mercury and Venus and probably the Earth too. In any case the Earth will be vaporized, and even the outer planets will be violently heated. Next, the Sun will become unstable, and will vary in its output before it throws off its outer layers altogether, and turns into what we call a planetary nebula – a bad term, because a star in stage has nothing whatsoever to do

with a planet and is not truly a nebula. Then the outer layers will move away into space and dissipate, leaving what is left of the Sun in the form of a small, dense core with all its atoms crushed and broken, so that they can be packed tightly together with almost no waste of space. The Sun will have become a white dwarf, no larger than a globe equal in size to Uranus or Neptune.

By then the luminosity will have fallen to less than one-thousandth of today's value, and over the ages it will drop still further, because the Sun will have no fuel left and will be bankrupt. The final state will be that of a cold, dead black dwarf, still circled by the ghosts of its remaining planets.

It is rather a gloomy picture, even though we have the comfort of knowing that the white dwarf stage will not begin for at least five thousand million years. Yet it does seem to be the pattern; we cannot see a star changing as it ages, but we can observe stars in different stages of evolution and work out what is happening. We can see very young stars, which have been born inside nebulæ and are still flickering irregularly as they condense; we can see many stars which are in the same condition as the Sun is today; we can see red giants, such as Betelgeux in Orion, which have swollen out after they have used up their hydrogen fuel, and we can see planetary nebulae, such as the Ring in the little constellation of Lyra, where the small, hot central star is surrounded by a shell of gas, giving the rather misleading impression of a tiny, shining cycle-tyre. White dwarfs are plentiful, though they are so dim that we cannot see them unless they are reasonably close to us. The most famous example is the companion of Sirius, the brightest star in the sky, which lies at a distance of only 8.6 light-years, and is the closest of all the brilliant stars apart from the southern Alpha Centauri. Sirius itself is 26 times as powerful as the Sun; the white dwarf companion has only $1/10,000$ the luminosity of its primary, and is no more than 38,600km (24,000 miles) in diameter. This means that it is at least 60,000 times as dense as water, and a spoonful of its material would weigh many tons. Its glory has departed; in the past it must have been a huge, powerful red giant.

The only characters in the story which we cannot see are the black dwarfs. We would not expect to do so, because they send out no energy at all, but in any case it is by not means certain whether the universe, in its present form, has existed for long enough for any black dwarfs to form. Stars take an immense period to reach this stage – possibly more than the 15,000 million to 20,000 million years since the Big Bang.

Finally, we must ask ourselves whether there is any escape. Certainly we cannot hope to alter the evolution of the Sun, but there may be other ways. In the few thousands of years which have elapsed since the start of what we usually call 'civilization' we have progressed from making stone axes to sending rockets to the planets, so that if we are left undisturbed for several thousands of millions of years there should be no limit

to what we can achieve. It may seem absurd to consider moving the Earth out of its orbit, or even providing it with a heat-source quite independent of the Sun, but – who knows?

Be this as it may, there is no imminent danger except from ourselves. We have ample time not only to colonize the Moon and other planets, but to make the best of our own Earth. It is the only world for us; let us make sure that we take good care of it.

One day the Earth will be engulfed in a few short seconds in a soundless explosion of light as the Sun throws off its outer layers in a final, cataclysmic outburst.

APPENDIX 1. THE EARTH

Diameter:	equatorial, 12,755km (7,926 miles). polar, 12,700km (7,899) miles.
Distance from the Sun:	maximum 152,239,780km (94,600,000 miles). mean 149,595,700km (92,957,000 miles). minimum 147,090,020km (91,400,000 miles).
Axial inclination::	23°.441.
Rotation period:	23h 56m 04s.
Revolution period:	365.256 days.
Escape velocity:	11.16km/sec (6.94 miles/sec).
Mean orbital velocity:	29.7km/sec (18.5 miles/sec).
Mass:	5.976×10^{24} kg.
Density, water = 1:	5.517.
Increase in the length of the 'day' due to tidal action:	0.0007 second per century.
Age:	4,600 million years.

APPENDIX 2. THE MOON

Diameter:	3,476km (2,160 miles).
Distance from Earth (surface to surface):	maximum 406,767km (252,760 miles). mean 384,460km (238,900 miles). minimum 356,395km (221,460 miles).
Axial inclination:	1°32'.
Rotation period:	27.321 days (27d 7h 43m).
Revolution period:	27.321 days (27d 7h 43m).
Synodic period (new moon to new moon):	29d 12h 44m.
Escape velocity:	2.38km/sec (1.48 miles/sec).
Mean orbital velocity:	0.96km/sec (0.6 miles/sec).
Mass, Earth = 1:	0.012. (1/81).
Volume, Earth = 1:	0.020.
Surface gravity, Earth = 1:	0.165.
Density, water = 1:	3.342.
Apparent diameter, seen from Earth:	maximum 33'31". mean 31'5". minimum 29'22".

APPENDIX 3. THE PLANETS

Name	Mean distance from Sun, millions of miles	Revolution period	Rotation period (equatorial)	Equatorial diameter, miles	Mass, Earth = 1	Escape velocity, miles/sec	Number of satellites
Mercury	36	88 days	58d 15h	3,030	0.06	2.6	0
Venus	67	224.7 days	243d	7,523	0.82	6.4	0
Earth	93	365.3 days	23h 56m	7,926	1	7	1
Mars	141.5	687 days	24h 37m	4,218	0.11	3.2	2
Jupiter	483	11.86 years	9h 51m	89,424	318	37	16
Saturn	886	29.40 years	10h 39m	74,914	95	22	17
Uranus	1783	84.01 years	17h 14m	31,770	15	14	15
Neptune	2793	164.79 years	16h 3m	31,410	17	15	8
Pluto	3666	247.70 years	6d 9h	1,199	0.002	0.7	1

To convert miles to kilometres, multiply by 1.6093

Index

Figures in *italic* refer to illustrations in the text

95

ACKNOWLEDGMENTS

Anglo-Australian Telescope Board: 14, 19, 91, 92.
Australian Overseas Information Service, London: 9.
Brian Trodd Publishing House: 46, 47 bottom.
D. Berry: 18, 86 bottom.
European Space Agency: 11, 84, 93.
IKI: 20.
J.Allan Cash Ltd.: 8, 10, 15, 16, 22, 24, 29, 31, 32 bottom, 34 top, 40, 41, 47 top, 55, 62, 79, 87
Jennifer Feller: 33.
JPL: 88, 89 top
NASA: 2, 3, 4, 5, 21, 37 bottom, 43, 49, 52, 53 left, 65, 68, 69 bottom, 73, 74, 75, 77, 81, 85, 86 top, 90.
Nicholas Booth/NASA: 12.
Nikk Burridge: 61 top.
Patrick Moore Collection: 23 bottom, 32 top, 38, 39, 42, 56, 59 and jacket, 63 top/bottom, 64, 66 top/bottom, 69 top, 70, 72, 78, 82/83.
Paul Doherty: 17, 28, 48, 50, 51, 57, 58 top, 60, 61 top, 80, 89 bottom.
RIDA: 26.
Science Photo Library: 23 top, 27, 30, 34 bottom, 35 top/bottom, 37 top, 42 bottom, 45 bottom, 53 right, 58 bottom, 61 bottom.
Starland Picture Library: 45 top.
TRH/NASA: 71